Classics.

# SWISS FAMILY ROBINSON

by

JOHANN WYSS

ABBEY CLASSICS
CRESTA HOUSE, LONDON

EDITED EDITION 1970


146/152, Holloway Road, London. N. 7

# CHAPTER I

Already the tempest had continued six terrible days, and far from subsiding on the seventh, its fury seemed to increase.

The masts had been shivered to pieces and cast into the sea; several leaks appeared, and the ship began to fill. "My children", said I, to my four boys, who clung to me in terrible alarm, "God can save us, for nothing is impossible to Him."

My excellent wife wiped the tears which were falling and encouraged the youngest children.

At this moment a cry of "Land! Land!" was heard through the roaring of the waves, and instantly the vessel struck against a rock with so violent a motion as to drive everyone from his place. The captain in a mournful voice called out that all was lost, and bade the men lose not a moment in putting out the boats.

I left my family and went on the deck. A wave instantly threw me down and wetted me to the skin; another followed, and then another. I steadied myself as well as I could, and when I could look around a scene of terrific and complete disaster met my eyes; the ship was split in two on one side. The ship's company crowded into the boats till they could contain not one man more, and the last who entered were now cutting the ropes to move off. I called to them with entreaties and prayers to stop and receive us also, but in vain; for the roaring of the sea prevented my being heard, and the waves, which rose to the height of mountains, would have made it impossible for a boat to return.

Sunk and desolate from the loss of every chance of human aid, it was yet my duty to make every effort to appear serene before my family. "Courage, dear ones," cried I on entering their cabin, "all is not yet lost! I will not conceal from you that the ship is aground, but we are at least in greater safety than we should be if she were beating upon the rocks: our cabin is above water, and should the sea be more calm tomorrow, we may yet find means to reach the land in safety."

My wife, however, more accustomed than the children to read my inmost thoughts, perceived the anxiety which devoured me.

"Let us take some nourishment," said she, "our courage will strengthen with our bodies; we shall perhaps need this comfort to support a long and melancholy night."

My dear wife had prepared our meal, and the four boys partook of it with an appetite to which their parents were strangers. They afterwards went to bed, and in a short time, in spite of the tempest, they were snoring soundly. Fritz, the eldest, sat up with us.

"I have been thinking," said he after a long silence, "how it may be possible to save ourselves. If we had only some instruments for swimming, some bladders or cork-jackets for my mother and my brothers, you and I, Father, would soon contrive to swim to land."

"That is a good thought," said I; "we will see if we can bring it to bear this very night, for fear of the worst."

Fritz and I immediately looked about for some small empty tubs or tin canisters. These we fastened two and two together with handkerchiefs or towels, leaving about a foot distance between them, attaching this sort of swimming-jacket under the arms of each child, my wife at the same time preparing one for herself.

We hailed with joy the first gleam of light which shot through a small opening of the window. The raging of the winds had begun to abate, the sky was become serene.

"Come along, my boys, let each go a different way about the ship, and see what he can do to be useful, and what he can find to enable us to get away," I said.

They now all sprang from me with eager looks to do what I had desired. My wife and the youngest boy visited all the animals, whom they found in a pitiable condition, and nearly perishing with hunger and thirst. Fritz repaired to the ammunition chamber, Ernest to the carpenter's cabin, and Jack to the apartment of the captain. Scarcely had Jack opened the door, when two large dogs sprang joyfully upon him, and nearly suffocated the boy with their affectionate licking of his face and hands in their delight at seeing a human being once more.

By and by, my little company were again assembled round me, each proud of what he had to contribute. Fritz had two fowling-pieces, some powder, and some small shot contained in horn flasks, and balls in bags. Ernest produced his hat filled with nails, and held in his hands a hatchet and a hammer; in addition, a pair of pincers, a pair of large scissors, and an auger peeped out of his pocket. Even the little six-year-old Francis carried under his arm quite a large box of fish-hooks, which were likely to be of great use to us.

"I, for my part," said my wife, "have brought nothing; but I have some tidings to communicate which I hope will secure my welcome. What I have to tell is, that I have found on board the ship a cow and an ass, two goats, six sheep, and a sow, all of whom I have just supplied with food and water, and I reckon on being able to preserve their lives."

I recollected having seen some empty casks in the hold. We went down, and found them floating about in the water, which almost filled the vessel. It cost us but little trouble to hoist them up and place them on the lower deck, which was at this time scarcely above water. They were exactly suited for our purpose, and with the assistance of my sons I instantly began to saw them in two. In a certain time I had produced eight tubs of equal size and of suitable height, which I contemplated with perfect satisfaction.

I then sought for a long plank capable of being a little curved at the ends. I fastened my eight tubs together, and then fixed on the plank by way of a keel. The tubs were nailed to each other, and, to make them the firmer, two other planks of the same length as the first were fixed on each side of the tubs. When all this was finished, we found we had produced a kind of boat which was divided into eight compartments, which I had no doubt would be able to perform a short course in calm water.

I bade Fritz fetch me a crowbar, who soon returned with it. I sawed a thick round pole into several pieces for rollers, and easily raised the foremost part of our boat with the crowbar, while Fritz placed one of the rollers under it.

I tied a long cord to its stern, and the other end of it to one of the timbers of the ship. We now put a second and a third roller under, and, applying the crowbar, to our great joy our contrivance descended into the water with such a velocity, that if the rope had not been well fastened it would have gone far out to sea.

There remained nothing more for me to do but to find out in what way I could get completely clear from the encumbrance of the wreckage that lay around us. I got into the first tub, and steered the head of our craft so as to make it enter the breach in the ship's side. I then got on board the ship again, and with saw and hatchet cleared away to right and left everything that could obstruct our passage. That being effected, we next secured some oars for our voyage the next morning.

We had spent the day in laborious exertions; it was already late, and as it would not have been possible to reach the land that evening, we were obliged to pass a second night in the wrecked vessel, which at every instant threatened to fall to pieces.

By break of day we were all awake and alert. When we had finished our morning prayer, I said:

"We now, with the assistance of Heaven, must enter upon the work of our deliverance. The first thing to be done is to give to each poor animal on board, before we leave them, a hearty meal; we will then put food enough before them to last for several days."

I decided that our first cargo should consist of a barrel of gunpowder, three fowling-pieces, and three carbines, with as much small shot and lead and as many bullets as our boat will bear; two pairs of pocket pistols and one of large ones, not forgetting a mould to cast balls in. We added a chest containing cakes of portable soup, another full of hard biscuits, an iron pot, a fishing-rod, a chest of nails and another of different tools, such as hammers, saws, pincers, hatchets, augers, and lastly some sail-cloth to make a tent.

When all was ready, we stepped bravely each into a tub. At the moment of our departure we heard all the cocks and hens begin to crow, as if they were conscious that we had deserted them, yet willing to bid us a sorrowful adieu. This suggested to me the idea of taking the geese, ducks, fowls, and pigeons with us, observing to my wife, that if we could not find means to feed them, at least they would feed us.

We accordingly executed this plan. We put ten hens and an old and a young cock into one of the tubs, and covered it with planks. We set the rest of the poultry at liberty, in the hope that instinct would direct them towards the land — the geese and the ducks by water, and the pigeons by the air.

We were waiting for my wife, who had the care of this last part of our embarkation, when she joined us loaded with a large bag, which she threw into the tub which already contained her youngest son. The order of our departure was as follows:

In the first tub, at the boat's head, my wife;

In the second, our little Francis, six years old, full of the happiest dispositions;

In the third, Fritz, our eldest boy, between fourteen and fifteen years of age, a handsome, curl-pated youth;

In the fourth was the barrel of gunpowder, with the cocks and hens and sail-cloth;

In the fifth, the provisions for the support of life;

In the sixth, my son Jack, a light-hearted, enterprising, generous lad, about ten years old;

In the seventh, my son Ernest, a boy of twelve years old, well informed, but somewhat disposed to indolence;

In the eighth, a father, to whose paternal care the task of guiding the craft for the safety of his beloved family was entrusted.

The tide was already at half its height when we left the ship; we rowed with all our strength. The two dogs we had left on board, plunged immediately into the sea and swam to the boat. They were too large for us to think of giving them admittance. Turk was an English dog, and Ponto of the Danish breed. I was in great uneasiness on their account, for I feared it would not be possible for them to swim so far. The dogs, however, managed the affair with perfect intelligence. When they found themselves fatigued. they rested their fore-paws on the paddles, which were now turned crossways.

Our voyage proceeded securely, though slowly. By and by, we perceived a little opening, near the mouth of a creek, towards which all our geese and ducks betook themselves; and I, relying on their sagacity, followed in the same course. This opening formed a little bay, the water of which was calm, and neither too deep nor too shallow to receive our boat. I entered it, and cautiously put on shore on a spot where the coast was about the same height above the water as our tubs, and where at the same time there was a quantity sufficient to keep us afloat.

All that had life in the boat jumped eagerly on land. Even little Francis, who had been wedged in his tub like a potted herring, now got up and sprang forward; but, with all his efforts, he could not succeed without his mother's help. The dogs, who had swum on shore, received us as if they were appointed to do the honours of the place, jumping round us with every demonstration of joy; the geese kept up a loud continual cackling, to which the ducks with their broad yellow beaks contributed a perpetual thorough bass; the cocks and hens, which we had already set at liberty, clucked; the boys chattering all at once produced altogether an overpowering confusion of sounds.

The first thing we did on finding ourselves safe on terra firma was to fall on our knees, and return thanks to the Supreme Being who had preserved our lives, and to recommend ourselves with entire resignation to the care of His paternal kindness.

We next employed our whole attention in unloading the boat. Oh, how rich we thought ourselves in the little we had been able to rescue from the merciless waters! We looked everywhere for a convenient place to erect a tent under the shade of the rocks; and having all consulted and agreed upon a place, we set to work. We drove one of our poles firmly into a fissure of the rock — this formed the ridge of our tent. We rested upon it another pole, and thus formed a frame for our dwelling. We next threw some sail-cloth over the ridge, and stretching it to a convenient distance on each side, fastened its extremities to the ground with stakes. I next desired my sons to look about and collect all the grass and moss they could find, and spread it to dry in the sun, as it would then serve us for beds. During this occupation, I erected at a small distance from the tent, and near a river, from which I hoped to be supplied with fresh water, a kind of little kitchen. A few flat stones that I found in the bed of the river served for a fireplace. I got a quantity of dry branches: with the largest I made a small enclosure round it; and with the little twigs, added to some of our turf, I made a brisk, cheering fire. We put some of the soup-cakes, with water, into our iron pot, and placed it over the fire; and my wife, with her little Francis for a scullion, took charge of preparing the dinner.

In the meanwhile Fritz had been reloading the guns, with one of which he had wandered along the side of the river. He had proposed to Ernest to accompany him, but Ernest replied that he did not like a rough and stony walk, and that he should go alone to the sea-shore. Jack took the road towards a chain of rocks which jutted out into the sea, with the intention of gathering some of the mussels which grew upon them.

While I was looking about, I heard loud cries proceeding from a short distance, and recognized the voice of Jack. I snatched my hatchet, and ran in an agony of apprehension to his assistance. I soon perceived him up to his knees in water, and that a large sea-lobster had fastened his claws in his leg. The poor boy screamed pitiably, and made useless efforts to disentangle himself. I jumped instantly into the water, and the enemy was no sooner sensible of my approach than he let go his hold, and would have been scampered out to sea. I turned quickly upon him, and took him up by the body and carried him off, followed by Jack, who shouted our triumph all the way. He begged me at last to let him hold the animal in his own hand, that he might himself present so fine a booty to his mother.

I picked up the lobster, and on Jack's entreaty let him carry it to the kitchen, which he entered, triumphantly exclaiming:

"Mama, Mama, a sea-lobster! Ernest, a sea-lobster! Where is Fritz? Where is Fritz? Take care, Francis, he will bite you!"

In a moment all were round him to examine the wonderful creature; and all proclaimed their astonishment at his enormous size, while they observed that its form was precisely that of the common lobster so much in use in Europe.

Soon after we had taken our meal the sun began to sink into the west. Our little flock of fowls assembled round us, pecking here and there what morsels of our biscuit had fallen to the ground. Just at this moment my wife produced the bag she had so mysteriously huddled into the tub. Its mouth was not opened; it contained the various sorts of grain for feeding poultry — barley, peas, oats, &c., and also different kinds of seeds of vegetables for the table. In the fulness of her kind heart she scattered several handfuls at once upon the ground, which the innocent creatures began eagerly to seize. I complimented her on the benefit her foresight had secured for us, but I recommended a more sparing use of so valuable an acquisition, observing that the grain, if kept for sowing, would produce a harvest, and that we could fetch from the ship spoiled biscuit enough to feed the fowls. Our pigeons sought a roosting place among the rocks; the hens, with the two cocks at their head, ranged themselves in a line along the ridge of the tent; and the geese and ducks betook themselves in a body, cackling and quacking as they proceeded, to a marshy bit of ground near the sea, where some thick bushes afforded them shelter.

A little later we ourselves began to follow the example of our winged companions by beginning our preparations for repose. First we charged our guns and pistols, and laid them carefully in the tent; next we assembled all together, and joined in offering up our thanks to the Almighty for the succour afforded us, and supplicating His watchful care for preservation.

## CHAPTER II

I was awaked at the first dawn of day by the crowing of the cocks. I awoke my wife, and we consulted together as to our occupation for the day. We both agreed that the thing of the most importance was to seek for such traces as might be found of our late ship companions, and at the same time to examine the nature of the soil on the other side of the river before we came to a determination about a fixed place of abode. My wife easily perceived that such an excursion could not be undertaken by all the members of the family; and, full of confidence in the protection of Heaven, she courageously consented to my proposal of my leaving her with the three youngest boys, and proceeding myself with Fritz on a journey of discovery.

In about an hour we had completed all that was necessary to be done previous to our departure, and were ready to set out. I had loaded the guns we left behind, and I now enjoined my wife to keep by day as near the boat as possible, which, in case of danger, was the best and most speedy means of escape.

The river we were about to pass was on each side so steep as to be inaccessible, except by one narrow slip near the mouth on one side, and from whence we had already drawn our supply of fresh water; but there was no means of effecting a passage across from this place, the opposite shore being an unbroken line of sharp, high, perpendicular rocks. We therefore walked on, following the course of the river till we arrived at an assemblage of rocks at which the stream formed a cascade: a few paces beyond we observed some large fragments of rock which had fallen into the bed of the river. By stepping upon these, and making now and then some hazardous leaps, we at length contrived to reach to the other side. We had proceeded a short way along the rock we ascended in landing, forcing ourselves a passage through overgrown grass mixed with other plants, and rendered more capable of resistance by being half dried up by the sun.

When we had walked about a hundred paces we heard a loud noise behind us as if we were pursued, and perceived a rustling motion in the grass, which was almost as tall as ourselves. I was well satisfied with the courage of Fritz, who, instead of being frightened and running away, stood still and firm to face the danger; the only motion he made being that of seeing that his piece was fit to be discharged, and turning himself to front the spot from whence the noise proceeded. Our alarm, however, was of short duration; for what was our joy on seeing rush out, not an enemy, but our faithful Turk, whom in the moment of departure we had quite forgotten, and whom no doubt our anxious relatives had sent to us!

When we had gone about two leagues we entered a wood situated a little farther from the sea. Here we threw ourselves on the ground, and under the shade of a tree, by the side of a clear running stream, took out some provisions and refreshed ourselves. We heard on every side around us the chirping, singing and the motion of unknown birds among the leaves, which in reality were more attractive by their splendid plumage than by any charm of note. Fritz assured me that between the branches of the bushes he saw some animals like apes.

We did not quit the wood, but pushed our way through it, being often obliged to cut a path through the bushes overrun by creeping plants with our hatchet. At length we reached a plain, which afforded a more extensive prospect and a path less perplexed and intricate.

We next entered a forest to the right, and soon observed in it here and there some trees of a particular species. Fritz, whose sharp eye was continually on a journey of discovery, remarked that some of them were of so very extraordinary an appearance that he could not resist the curiosity he felt to examine them closely.

"Look here, Father," he exclaimed. "What a singular kind of tree, with wens growing all about the trunk!"

We walked up to some of them, and I perceived with surprise and satisfaction that they were of the gourd-tree kind the trunks of which bear fruit. Fritz, who had never heard of such a tree, could not conceive the meaning of what he saw, and asked me if the fruit was a sponge or a wen.

"We will see," I replied, "if we cannot unravel the mystery. Try to get down one of them, and we will examine it minutely."

"I have got one," cried Fritz, "and it is exactly like a gourd, only the rind is thicker and harder."

"It then, like the rind of that fruit, can be used for making various utensils," observed I; "plates, dishes, basins, and flasks. We will give this tree the name of the gourd-tree."

Fritz jumped for joy.

"Hurrah!" cried he in ecstasy. "How happy Mother will be! She will no longer have the vexation when she makes soup of thinking that we shall scald our fingers."

"What, my boy, do you think is the reason that this tree bears its fruit only on the trunk and on its topmost branches?"

"I think it must be because the middle branches are too feeble to support such a weight."

"You have guessed exactly right."

We next proceeded to the manufacture of our plates and dishes. I taught my son how to divide the gourd with a bit of string, which would cut

"We must leave them here on the sand for the sun to dry them thoroughly; this will be accomplished by the time of our return this way, and we can then carry them with us; but care must be taken to fill them with sand, that they may not shrink or warp in so ardent a heat."

While these different conversations and our labours had been going on, we had not neglected the great object of our pursuit, — the making every practicable search for our ship companions. But all, alas! was in vain.

After a walk of about four leagues in all, we arrived at a spot where a slip of land reached far out into the sea, on which we observed a hill or rising ground of considerable height.

We did not reach the top of the hill without much hard climbing, but when there it presented a magnificent scene of wild and solitary beauty, over a vast extent of land and water. It was, however, in vain that we made use of our spy-glass; no trace of man appeared.

I remarked to Fritz that we seemed destined to a solitary life, and that it was a rich country which appeared to be allotted us for a habitation; at least our habitation it must be, unless some vessel should happen to put on shore on the same coast, and be in a condition to take us back to our native land.

We descended from the hill, and having regained the shore we made our way to the wood of palms, which I had just pointed out to Fritz; but not without considerable difficulty, for our path lay through a quantity of reeds, entwined with other plants, which greatly obstructed our march. I cut myself a stalk of the reeds of uncommon length and more equally than a knife. I tied the string round the middle of the gourd as tight as possible, striking it pretty hard with the handle of my knife, and I drew tighter and tighter till the gourd fell apart, forming two regular-shaped bowls or vessels.

Fritz was in the utmost astonishment at my success. "I cannot imagine, Father," said he, "how this way of cutting the gourd could occur to you."

"I have read the description of such a process," replied I, "in books of travels, and also, that such of the savages as have no knives, and who make a sort of twine from the bark of trees, are accustomed to use it for this purpose. So you see what benefit may be derived from reading, and from afterwards reflecting on what we read."

"And the flasks, Father; in what manner are they made?"

"For this branch of their ingenuity the savages make preparation a long time beforehand. If a negro wishes to have a flask or bottle with a neck, he ties a very young gourd round in the proper place with a piece of string, of linen, bark of the tree, or anything he can get hold of; he draws this bandage so tight, that the part at liberty soon forms itself to a round shape, while the part which is confined contracts, and remains over after narrow. By this method it is that they obtain flasks or bottles of a perfect form."

Our conversation and our labour thus went on together. Fritz had completed some plates, and was not a little proud of the achievement. "Ah, how delighted my mother will be to eat upon them!" cried he. "But how shall we convey them to her? They will not, I fear, bear travelling well."

thickness. It was not without astonishment that I received a glutinous kind of sap proceed from the dividend end of the stalk. Prompted by curiosity, I tasted the sap, and found it sweet and of an agreeable flavour, so that not a doubt remained in my mind that we were passing through a fine plantation of sugar-canes.

I determined not to tell Fritz immediately of the fortunate discovery I had made, preferring that he should find the pleasure out for himself. As he was at some distance on before, I called out to him to cut a reed for his defence. This he instantly did, and, without any remark, used it simply for a stick, striking lustily with it on all sides to clear a passage. This motion occasioned the sap to run out abundantly. He now tasted what was on his fingers. "Father, Father! I have found some sugar! some syrup! I have a sugar-cane in my hand!"

In the meantime Fritz eagerly devoured the cane he had cut.

"I will take home a good provision of sugar-canes, Father. I shall only just taste of them once or twice as I walk along. But it will be so delightful to regale my mother and my little brothers with them!"

"Certainly, Fritz; but do not take too heavy a load, for recollect you have other things to carry, and we have yet far to go."

Counsel was given in vain. He persisted in cutting at least a dozen of the largest canes, tore off their leaves, tied them together, and, putting them under his arm, dragged them as well as he was able through thick and thin to the end of the plantation. We arrived without accident at the wood of palms, which we entered in search of a place of shade, where we might stretch our limbs on the ground and finish our repast. We were scarcely settled, when suddenly a great number of large monkeys, terrified by the sight of us and the barking Turk, stole so nimbly and yet so quietly up the trees, that we scarcely perceived them till they had reached the topmost parts. From this height they fixed their eyes upon us, grinding their teeth, making most horrible grimaces, and saluting us with frightful screams of hostile import. I observed that the trees were palms, bearing cocoa-nuts, and I instantly conceived the hope of obtaining some of this fruit in an unripe and milky state by help of the monkeys.

I now began to throw some stones at the monkeys. With their accustomed habit of imitation they furiously tore off, nut by nut, all that grew upon the branches near them, to hurl them down upon us, so that it was with difficulty we avoided the blows; and in a short time a large quantity of cocoa-nuts lay on the ground round us. We chose a place where we could repose at our ease to regale ourselves on this rich harvest. We opened the shells with a hatchet, but not without having first enjoyed the sucking of some of the milk through the three small holes, round which we found it easy to insert a knife and let the milk escape. The milk of the cocoa-nut has not in reality a very pleasant flavour, but it is excellent for quenching violent thirst. What we liked best was a kind of solid cream which adheres to the shell and which we scraped off with our spoons. We mixed with it a little of the sap of our sugar-canes, and it made a delicious repast.

Our meal being finished, we prepared to leave the place. I tied together such of the cocoa-nuts as had retained the stalks, and threw them across my shoulder. Fritz resumed his bundle of sugar-canes. We divided the rest of the things between us, and continued our way towards home.

My poor boy now began to complain of fatigue. The bundle of sugar-canes galled his shoulders, and he was obliged to move it from place to place. At last he stopped to take breath.

"I never could have thought," cried he, "that a few sugar-canes could be so heavy. How I pity the poor negroes who carry them in even larger bundles, and for greater distances! I should, however, be so glad to get them home to Mother and my brothers."

"But I am not without apprehensions, Fritz, that of our acquisition we shall carry them only a few sticks for firewood, for I must bring to recollection the circumstance that the juice of the sugar-cane is apt to turn sour soon after cutting, and the more likely is this in such heat as we now experience. We may suck them, therefore, without compunction, and without regret at the diminution of our number of canes."

"Well, then, if we can do no better with the sugar-canes," said Fritz, "at least I will take them a good supply of the milk of cocoa-nuts, which I have here in a tin bottle. We shall sit round on the grass and drink is so deliciously!"

"In this too, my boy, I fear you will also be disappointed. You talk of milk, but the milk of the cocoa-nut, no less than the juice of the sugar-cane, when exposed to the air and heat, turns soon to vinegar.

I fear very much it is already sour, for the tin bottle which contains it is particularly liable to become hot in the sun."

"Oh, dear, how provoking!" groaned poor Fritz. "I must taste it this very minute."

The tin bottle was lowered from his shoulder in the twinkling of an eye, and he began to pull the cork with all his strength. As soon as it was loose the liquid flew upwards in a brisk stream, and with a loud noise and frothing like champagne.

"Bravo, Mr. Fritz! You have manufactured there a wine of some mettle. I must now caution you not to let it make you tipsy."

"Oh, taste it, Father, pray taste it! It is quite delicious; not the least like vinegar. It is really like wine; its taste is sweet, and it is so sparkling! Do take a little, Father! Is it not good? If all the milk remains in this state the treat will be better than even I thought."

The cocoa-nut wine, for so Fritz named it, gave our exhausted frames an increase of strength and cheerfulness, and we pursued our way with briskness to the place where we had left our gourd utensils upon the sands. We found them perfectly dry, as hard as bone, and not the least mis-shapen. We now, therefore, could put them into our game-bags conveniently enough; and this done, we continued our way. Scarcely had we passed through the little wood in which we breakfasted, when Turk sprang furiously upon a troop of monkeys, and before we could get to the spot our ferocious Turk had already seized one of them. It was a female monkey, who held a young one in her arms. The pour creature was killed. The young one hid himself in the grass and looked on.

grinding his teeth all the time that this horrible achievement was performing.

Fritz flew like lightning to force the ferocious Turk from his prey.

The next scene that presented itself was of a different nature, and comical enough. The young monkey, on perceiving Fritz, sprang nimbly on his shoulders, and fastened his feet securely in the stiff curls of his hair; nor could the squalls of Fritz, nor all the shaking he gave, make the little creature let go his hold. I ran to Fritz, laughing heartily, for I saw that the animal was too young to be capable of doing him any injury.

"There is no remedy, Fritz," said I, "but to submit quietly and carry him."

"But I assure you, Father," cried Fritz, "he is giving me some terrible twitches. Do try to get him off!"

With a little gentleness and management I at last succeeded. I took the creature in my arms as one would an infant, and I confess I could not help pitying and caressing him. He was not larger than a kitten, and quite unable to help himself.

"Father," cried Fritz, "do let me have this little animal in my own keeping. I will take the greatest care of him. I will give him all my share of the milk of the cocoa-nuts till we get our cows and goats. And, who knows? His monkey instinct may one day assist us in discovering some different kinds of wholesome fruits."

"I have not the least objection," answered I. "It is but just that the little dependent should be given up to your management and discretion."

In happy expectation of our return, we forgot the length of our journey, and found ourselves on the bank of the river before we were aware, and shortly after our much-loved family appeared in sight on the opposite shore, exhibiting every demonstration of unbounded joy at our safe return. They advanced along by the course of the river, till they on one side and we on the other had reached the place where we had crossed it in the morning. We repassed it again in safety and greeted each other with joy. Scarcely had the young ones joined their brother that they began their exclamations of surprise.

"A monkey, a live monkey! Father, Mother, a live monkey! Oh, how delightful! How happy shall we be! How did you catch him? What a droll face he has!"

"His is very ugly!" said little Francis, half afraid to touch him.

"He is much prettier than you!" retorted Jack. "Only see, he is laughing! I wish I could see him eat!"

"Ah! If we had but some cocoa-nut!" said Ernest. "Could you not find any? Are they nice?"

"Have you brought me any milk of almonds?" said Francis.

"Have you met with any unfortunate adventure?" asked my wife.

In this manner questions and exclamations succeeded to each other without interval, and with such rapidity as not to leave us time to answer them.

Jack received my gun, Ernest the cocoa-nuts, Francis the gourd-rinds, and my wife my game-bag. Fritz distributed the sugar-canes, at the same time begging Ernest to relieve him of his gun. But Ernest, ever careful of his own accommodation, assured him that the large heavy bowls with which he was loaded were the most he had strength to carry. His mother, a little too indulgent to his lazy humour, relieved him of them. Thus we proceeded altogether to our tent.

Fritz whispered me that if Ernest had known what the large heavy bowls were he would not so readily have parted with them. Then, turning to his brother, "Why, Ernest," cried he, "do you know that these bowls are cocoa-nuts, your dear much-desired cocoa-nuts and each containing the sweet nice milk you have so much wished to taste?"

"Are they indeed? Are they really and truly cocoa-nuts? Oh, Mother, return them to me quickly! I will carry them, if you please; and I can carry the gun too without finding it heavy!"

"No, no, Ernest," answered his mother. "I do not intend to be teased with hearing any more of your heavy sighs and moanings about your being fatigued, for I am certain you would begin again before we had gone a hundred paces."

Ernest would willingly have asked his mother to give him the cocoa-nuts and take the gun herself, but this he dare not do. "I have only," said he, "to get rid of these sticks, and carry the gun in my hand."

"I would advise you not to give up the sticks either," said Fritz drily. "I know you will be sorry if you do, and for this good reason — the sticks are sugar-canes!"

"Sugar-canes!" cried Ernest. "Sugar-canes!" exclaimed they all; and surrounding Fritz, made him give them full instructions on the sublime art of sucking sugar-canes.

My wife, also, who had always entertained a high respect for the article of sugar in her household management, was perfectly astonished, and earnestly entreated we would explain to her all about it. I instantly complied with her request, giving her every explanation and particular respecting our journey, and our new acquisitions, which I alternately exhibited for her inspection, no one of which afforded her more pleasure than the plates and dishes. We now adjourned to our little kitchen, and with great delight observed the preparations going forward in it for supper. On one side of the fire we saw a turnspit, which my wife had contrived by driving two forked pieces of wood into the ground, and placing a long even stick sharpened at one end across them. By this invention she was enabled to toast different kinds of fish or other food, with the help of little Francis, who was entrusted with the care of turning it round from time to time. On the occasion of our return she had prepared us the treat of a goose, the fat of which ran down into some oyster-shells placed there to serve the purpose of a dripping-pan. There was also a dish of fish which the little ones had caught, and the iron pot was upon the fire, provided with a good soup, the agreeable odour of which increased our appetite.

Fritz asked me if he might not invite our company to taste his fine champagne, which he said would not fail to make us all the merrier. "I have not the least objection," answered I, "but remember to taste it yourself before you serve it to your guests."

He ran to draw out the stopple, and to taste it... "How unfortunate!" said he. "It is already turned to vinegar!"

"What is it? — vinegar did you say?" exclaimed my wife. "How lucky! It will make the most delicious sauce for our bird, mixed with the fat which has fallen from it in roasting, and will be as good a relish as a salad."

By the time we had finished our meal the sun was retiring from our view, and recollecting how quickly the night would fall upon us, we were in the greatest haste to regain our place of rest. My wife had considerately procured for us a tenfold quantity of dry grass, which she had spread in the tent, so that we anticipated with joy the prospect which was now afforded of stretching our limbs on a substance somewhat approaching to the quality of mattresses, while the night before our bodies seemed to lie on the hard ground. We now all lay down upon the grass in the order of the night before, myself remaining last to fasten the sail-cloth in front of the tent, when, heartily fatigued by the exercise and exertions of the day, I as well as the rest soon fell into a profound and refreshing sleep.

## CHAPTER III

We awakened early the next morning.

The first thing thought of was breakfast, for the appetites of young boys open with their eyes. Today their mother had nothing to give them for their morning meal but some biscuits, which was so hard and dry that it was with difficulty we could swallow it. This decided me on taking Fritz out to the wreck to see what luxuries may yet lie in her.

While Fritz was getting the boat ready I looked about for a pole, and put a piece of white linen to the end of it. This I drove into the ground, in a place where it would be visible from the vessel. I agreed with my wife that in case of any accident that should require my immediate presence, they should take down the pole and fire a gun three times as a signal of distress, in consequence of which I would immediately return. But I gave her notice, that there being so many things to do on board the vessel, it was very probable that we should not be able to return the same day; in which case I, on my part, also promised to make them signals. My wife had the courage and the good sense to consent to my plan.

We embarked in silence, often looking back at the dear ones we were quitting. Fritz rowed steadily, and I did my best to second his endeavours by rowing from time to time with the oar which served me for a rudder.

Little as I knew of the management of sea affairs, I succeeded in keeping our boat in the direction in which the current ran, by which means we were drawn gently on, till the current had conducted us to within a short distance of the wreck without our having any other trouble than that of keeping our direction.

A little afterwards we found ourselves safely arrived at the breach of the vessel, and fastened our boat securely to one of the timbers.

Scarcely had we got out of the boat than Fritz proceeded with his young monkey on his arm to the main deck, where he found all the animals we had left on board assembled. I followed him with great readiness, well pleased to observe the generous impatience he betrayed to relieve the wants of the poor abandoned creatures. We next examined the food and water of the other animals, taking away what was half-spoiled and adding a fresh supply. Nor did we neglect the care of renewing our own strength by a plentiful repast.

While we were seated and appeasing the calls of hunger, Fritz and I consulted what should be our first occupation, when, to my great surprise, the advice he gave was that we should, immediately contrive a sail for our boat. "What," cried I, "makes you think of such a thing at so critical a moment, and when we have so many other things of indispensable necessity to arrange."

"Father," said Fritz; "let me confess the truth, which is, that I found it very difficult to perform the task of rowing. I observed that, though the wind blew strong in my face, the current nevertheless carried us on. Now, as we cannot be benefited on our return by the current, I was thinking that we might make the wind supply its place. Our boat will be very heavy when we have loaded it with all the useful things we mean to take away, and I am afraid I shall not be strong enough to row to land. Now, do you not think that a sail would be of great assistance?"

"Ah ha, Mr. Fritz! So you wish to spare yourself a little trouble, do you? But to speak seriously, I perceive a great deal of good sense in your argument, and think myself much obliged to my privy counsellor for his good advice. The best thing we can do is to take care and not overload the boat, and thus avoid the danger of sinking, or of being obliged to throw some of our stores overboard. Come then, let us set to work upon your sail, which, if it saves your labour in rowing, will be at least a little troublesome at present. Come along, and let us look about for what we want."

I assisted Fritz to carry a pole strong enough to serve for a mast, and another not so thick for a sail-yard. I directed him to make a hole in a plank with an auger, large enough to make a triangular sail; in the edges I made holes, and passed cords through them. I then sought for a pulley, that I might fasten it to the top of the mast, and thus be enabled to raise and lower my sail at pleasure.

While I was thus occupied, Fritz had been taking observations through a telescope of what was passing on land. He imparted the agreeable tidings that all was still well with our dear family. He had distinguished his mother walking tranquilly along the shore. He soon after brought me a small streamer which he had cut from a piece of linen, and which he entreated me to tie to the extremity of the mast, and he appeared as much delighted with the streamer as with the sail itself.

"But now, Father," said Fritz, looking kindly on me as he spoke, "as you have eased me of the labour of rowing, it is my turn to take care of you. I am thinking about making a better rudder; one that would enable you to steer the boat both with greater ease and greater safety."

"Your thought would be a very good one," said I, "but that I am unwilling to lose the advantage of being able to proceed this way and that, without being obliged to veer. I shall, therefore, fix our oars in such a manner as to enable me to steer the raft from either end."

During these exertions the day became far advanced, and I perceived that we should be obliged to pass the night in our tubs, not having as yet entered upon our task of emptying the vessel. We had promised our family to hoist a flag as a signal of our intention to pass the night from home, and we decided that our streamer was precisely the thing we wanted for this purpose.

We employed the rest of the day in emptying the tubs of the useless ballast of stone, and putting in their place what would be of service, such as nails, pieces of cloth, and different kinds of utensils

The vessel, which was now a wreck, had been sent out as a preparation for the establishment of a colony in the South Seas, and for that reason had been provided with a variety of stores not commonly included in the loading of a ship. The quantity of useful things which presented themselves in the store-chambers made it difficult for me to select among them, and I much regretted that circumstances compelled me to leave some of them behind. Fritz, however, already meditated a second visit. We descended to the kitchen, which we stripped of gridirons, kettles, pots of all kinds, a small roasting-jack, &c. Our last prize was a chest of choice eatables, intended for the table of the officers, containing Westphalia hams, Bologna sausages, and other savour food. I took good care not to forget some little sacks of maize, of wheat, and other grain, and some potatoes. We next added such implements for husbandry as we could find: shovels, hoes, spades, rakes, harrows &c.

Our cargo was so considerable that the tubs were filled to the very brim, and no inch of the boat's room was lost. The first and last of the tubs were reserved for Fritz and me to seat ourselves in and row the boat, which sunk so low in the water that, if the sea had been otherwise than quite calm, we should have been obliged to ease her of some of the loading: we, however, used the precaution of putting on our swimming-jackets for fear of any misfortune.

It will easily be imagined that every moment of the day had been laboriously employed. Night suddenly surprised us, and it was no longer possible to think of returning to our family the same evening.

After offering up our earnest prayers for the safety and happiness of all, yet not without some apprehension for the night, we resigned ourselves to sleep in our tubs, which, it must be confessed, did not afford us a very enviable place of rest.

Early the next morning, though it was scarcely light enough to distinguish the coast, I was already on the deck of the ship, endeavouring to have a sight of the tent through a spying-glass. Fritz speedily prepared a good substantial breakfast of biscuit and ham; but before we sat down to this refreshment, we recollected that in the captain's cabin we had seen a telescope of a much superior size and power, and we hastily conveyed it upon the deck. While this was doing, the brightness of the day had succeeded to the imperfect light of an earlier hour. I eagerly fixed my eye to the glass, and discovered my wife coming out of the tent and looking attentively towards the vessel, and we at the same moment perceived the motion of the flag upon the shore. A load of care and solicitude was thus taken from my heart; for now I had obtained the certainty that the beloved beings I had left were all in good health, and had escaped the dangers of the night. A great object of my anxiety now was to endeavour to save the livestock and get them to shore.

"I think, Father, we should tie a long rope round the sow's neck and throw her into the sea. She is sure to be able to swim, and we can easily get hold of the other end of the rope and draw her after the boat. Then here is another idea, Father: let us tie a swimming-jacket round the body of each animal, and throw them into the water; you will see that they will swim like fish, and we can draw them after the boat," and thus spoke Fritz.

We accordingly hastened to carry out our design. We fixed on a jacket to one of the lambs and threw it into the sea, and full of fear, of hope, and anxious curiosity, I followed the poor animal with my eyes. He sunk at first under water, and I thought he was drowned; but he soon reappeared, shaking the water from his head, and in a few seconds we perceived that he could swim quite well.

We then went and looked out four small casks, such as had been used for keeping the fresh water for the vessel. I bound them together with a large piece of sail-cloth. I strengthened this with a second piece of sail-cloth, and this contrivance I destined to support the cow and the ass, two casks to each, the animal being placed in the middle with a cask on either side, and thus, in less than an hour, both my cow and my ass were equipped for swimming.

It was next the turn of the smaller animals. Of these, it was the sow who gave us the most trouble; we were first obliged to put a muzzle on her to prevent her biting, and this being done, we tied a large piece of cork under her body. The sheep and goats were more docile, and we had soon accoutred them for the expedition. And now we had succeeded in assembling our whole company on the deck, in readiness for the voyage. We tied a cord to either the horns or the neck of each animal, and to the other end of the cord a piece of wood. We struck away some more of the shattered pieces of wood from the side of the vessel, and, one by one, coaxed our livestock into the sea.

We had now not a moment to lose; our last act was to put on our cork-jackets, and then we descended without accident through the breach, took our station in the boat, and were soon out to sea, surrounded by our troop of quadrupeds. We carefully took up from the water each of the floating bits of wood which we had fastened to the ends of the ropes round the animals, and thus drew them all after us by fastening the bits of timber to the boat. When everything was adjusted and our company in order, we hoisted our sail, which, soon filling with a favourable wind, conducted us and our escort safe to the land.

A sudden exclamation from Fritz filled me with alarm. "Oh, Father," cried he, "look! A fish of an enormous size is coming up to the boat!"

"Be ready with your gun, Fritz, and the moment he is close upon us, let us both fire upon him at the same instant."

Fritz aimed his fire so skilfully that the ball lodged in the head of the monster, which was an enormous shark. The fish half turned himself round in the water and hurried off to sea, leaving us to observe the lustrous smoothness of his belly, and that as he proceeded he stained the water red, which convinced us he had been severely wounded.

I resumed the rudder, and as the wind drove us straight towards the bay, I took down the sail and continued rowing till we reached a convenient spot for our cattle to land. I then untied the end of the cords, which had been fastened to the boat, and they stepped contentedly on shore. Our voyage thus happily concluded, we followed their example. My wife could find no words to express her surprise and satisfaction at seeing so many useful animals round us.

"I had been ransacking my poor brains," said she, "every moment of your absence, to conceive some means by which you might succeed in protecting the poor animals, but I could fix on none that seemed to promise the least success."

Perceiving that no preparations were making for supper, I ordered Fritz to bring us the Westphalia ham. The eyes of all were now fixed upon me with astonishment, everyone believing I could only be in jest. Fritz returned, jumping and displaying with exultation a large and excellent ham, which we had begun to cut in the morning.

"A ham!" cried one and all, clapping their hands. "A ham! and ready dressed! What a nice supper we shall have!"

"It comes quite in the nick of time too," said I, "for to judge by appearances, a certain careful steward I could name seems to have intended to send us supperless to bed, little thinking, I suppose, that a long voyage by water is apt to increase the appetite."

"I will tell you presently," replied my wife "what it was that prevented me from providing a supper for you all at an earlier hour. Your ham, however, makes you ample amends, and I have something in my hand which will make a pretty side-dish." She now showed me about a dozen of turtles' eggs, and then hurried away to make an omelette of some of them.

When we had finished our repast, I bade Fritz present our company with a bottle of Canary wine, which we had brought from the captain's cabin, and I then desired my wife would tell us all that had befallen them while Fritz and I had been on the ship. I first requested her to taste our wine, and then she began her narrative.

"Well," said my wife, with a smile, "on the first day of your absence nothing took place, except that we were anxious on your account. But this morning, I looked about before the boys were up, in hopes to find a shady place in which I might sit down and rest myself; but not a shady spot could I find, for there is not a single tree near us, and the only bit of shade which presented itself was behind our tent. This occasioned me to reflect a little seriously on our situation. Why not undertake, with my younger sons, to do something that shall add some one comfort to our existence? I determined to share a slight dinner with the boys, and courageously to set out on a journey of discovery for a habitation which might afford us more convenience, and a better shelter from the sun.

"I next assembled them all three around me, and informed them of my plans for an excursion, and you may believe I heard nothing like a dissenting voice. They lost not a moment in preparing for our departure; they examined their arms, their game-bags, looked out the best clasp-knives, and cheerfully undertook to carry the provision-bags. I, for my share, was loaded with a large flask of water and a hatchet, for which I thought it likely we might find a use. I also took the light gun which belongs to Ernest, and gave him a small carbine. We took some refreshment and then sallied forth attended by the two dogs for an escort. We arrived at the place at which you had crossed the river, and succeeded in passing over as securely as you had done, not, however, without considerable difficulty.

"As we advanced, I reflected that our safety depended in some measure on the two boys, because it was they only who knew how to use the guns. I now for the first time began to feel how fortunate it was that you had accustomed them from infancy to face danger of every kind.

"Ernest was first in reaching the other side, and met with no accident. After having filled my flask with river-water, we proceeded on our way; and when we had reached to the top of the ascent on the other side, which you described to us as so enchanting, I myself experienced the same delight from the scenery around.

"We were interrupted by the extraordinary height and thickness of the grass, which we had great difficulty in getting through.

"Continuing our journey, we reached the little wood and here our son Ernest had an opportunity of recognizing many of the originals of the engravings in his books of natural history. You must somehow have missed this wood, or so extraordinary a sight could not have escaped your observation. In my whole life I have never seen a single tree of so immense a size. What appeared to us at a distance to be a wood, was only a group of about fourteen of them, the trunks of which looked as if they were supported in their upright position by so many arches on each side, the arches being formed by portions of the roots of the tree, of great thickness and extent. Meanwhile the tree itself is further supported by a perpendicular root, placed in the midst of the others, and of a smaller compass, while the projecting roots extend themselves on every side of the tree, and double the circumference it would have.

"Jack climbed with considerable trouble upon one of these arch-formed roots, and with a pack-thread in his hand measured its circumference, which he found was some twenty-two inches and a half. I made thirty-two steps in going round one of those giant trees at the roots. The twigs of this tree are strong and thick; its leaves moderately large in size, and bearing some resemblance to the hazel-tree of Europe; but I was unable to discover that it bore any fruit. The soil immediately round the tree and under its branches produced in great abundance a short thick kind of plant, unmixed with any of the thistle kind, and of a perfectly smooth surface. Thus every circumstance seemed to concur in inviting us to use this spot as a place of repose, and my predilection for it grew so strong that I resolved to go no farther, but to enjoy its delicious coolness till it should be time to return.

"When we had shared our dinner among us, and well rested from our fatigue, we set out on our return, again keeping close to the river, half expecting to see along the shore some of the pieces or other vestiges of the vessel which the waves might have washed on shore there."

My dear wife's story finished, I assured her how much I admired her courage.

"Tell me," said I, "if I shall make you a balloon of sail-cloth, to enable you to arrive at your country-seat amongst the branches?"

"Yes, yes," said she, "laugh as much as you like, but I assure you my plan is not so silly as you imagine. Do you recollect the large lime-tree in the public walk of the town we lived in, and the pretty little room which had been built among its branches, and the flight of stairs which led to it? What should hinder us from effecting such a contrivance in one of my giant trees, which afford even better facilities in the enormous size and strength of their branches, and the peculiar manner of their growth?"

"I think it is a very good idea," said I, "and we must see what we can do to build ourselves a house in the trees."

## CHAPTER IV

When my wife and I were awake next morning we resumed the question of our change of abode. I observed to her that it was a matter of great difficulty.

"First," I said, "we must contrive a place among the rocks where we can leave our provisions and other things, which may serve both for a fortress and a storehouse, and to which, in case of any danger from invasion in the wood, we can immediately retreat. Come then, this agreed, the next thing is to throw a bridge across the river, if we are to pass it with all our family and baggage."

"Well, a bridge let there be," said my wife. "But let us not allow ourselves a moment of leisure till we have completed all that is necessary for our departure."

I prepared the boat for another journey to the vessel, to bring away a sufficient quantity of planks and timbers for the bridge. After breakfast we set out; and this time I took with me Ernest as well as Fritz, that we might accomplish our object in a shorter time. We rowed stoutly till we reached the current, which soon drew us on beyond the bay; but scarcely had we passed a little islet lying to one side of us, than we perceived a prodigious quantity of sea-gulls and other birds. I therefore steered to the spot, but finding that the boat made but little way, I hoisted my sail that we might have the assistance of the wind.

To Ernest our expedition afforded the highest delight. He was in ecstasies at seeing the sail begin to swell, and the motion of the streamer in the air. Fritz on his part did not for a moment take his eyes from the islet where the birds had assembled.

I approached sufficiently near to step upon the land, and after bringing the boat to an anchor with a heavy stone, we walked cautiously and gently up to the birds. We soon perceived that the object which attracted them was in reality an enormous fish, which has been thrown by the sea upon the islet. Fritz did not cease to express his wonder at the monstrous size of the animal, and asked me by what means he could have got there.

"I believe," answered I, "you were yourself the means; there is every appearance that it is the very shark you wounded yesterday. See here are the two balls which you discharged at its head."

"I do believe it is the very same!" cried Fritz, skipping about for joy. "I well remember I had two balls in my gun, and here they are, lodged in his hideous head!"

"I grant it is hideous enough," continued I. "See what a horrible mouth he has, and what a rough and prickly skin! One might almost use it for a file. Nor is he small of his kind, for I fancy that he measures more than twenty feet, from head to tail. But let us each take away with us a bit of his skin, for I have an idea that it may in some way or other be useful to us."

Fritz and I then advanced and cut several long strips of the skin from the head of the shark, with which we were proceeding to our boat, when I observed, lying on the ground, some planks and timbers which had recently been cast by the sea on this little island. I, therefore, made choice of such as seemed proper for my purpose; and, with the assistance of the crowbar and a lever which we had brought with us, I found means to get them into the boat, and thus spared ourselves the trouble of proceeding farther to the vessel. I bound the timbers together, with the planks upon them, in the manner of a raft, and tied them to the end of the boat; so that, in consequence of this adventure, we were ready to return in about four hours after our departure, and might with justice boast of having done a good day's work. I accordingly pushed again for the current, which soon drove us out to sea. Then I tacked about, and resumed the direct route for the bay and for our place of embarkation, by this means avoiding the danger of touching upon shallows. All this succeeded to my utmost wishes; I unfurled my sail, and a brisk wind soon conveyed us to our landing-place.

Presently, we were once more landed safely on our shore, but no one of our family appeared. We called out to them as loud as we could, which was answered by the same sounds in return, and in a few minutes my wife appeared between her two little boys returning from the river, a rising piece of ground having concealed her from our sight.

"Now then, boys," said I, "the first thing is to see if our timbers are long enough to reach to the other side. By my eye I should think they are."

"Mother has some balls of packthread with which she measured the height of the giant tree," interrupted Ernest, "and nothing would be more easy than to tie a stone to the end of one of them and throw it on to the other side of the river; then we could draw it to the very brink, and thus obtain the exact length that would be required for our timbers."

"Your idea is excellent," cried I. "Nothing gives me more pleasure than to see you exercise your invention. Run quickly and fetch the packthread."

He returned without loss of time. The stone was tied to its end and thrown across as we had planned. We drew it gently back to the river edge, marking the place where the bridge was to rest. We next measured the string, and found that the distance from one side to the other was eighteen feet. It appeared to me necessary, that to give sufficient solidarity to the timbers, I must allow three feet at each end of extra length for fixing them, amounting therefore in all to twenty-four feet; and I was fortunate enough to find that several of those we had brought did not fall short of this length.

Having consulted together as to the means of laying our timbers across the river, the first thing I did was to attach one of them to the trunk of a tree by a strong cord, long enough to turn freely round the trunk. I then fastened another cord to the other end of the beam. This cord I fastened round a stone, and then threw the stone across the river. I next passed the river as I had done before, furnished with a pulley, which I secured to a tree. I passed my second cord through the pulley, and recrossing the river with this cord in my hand, I contrived to harness the ass and the cow to the end of the cord. I next drove the animals from the bank of the river. They resisted at first, but I made them go by force of drawing. I first fixed one end of the beam firm to the trunk of the tree, and then they drew along the other end, so as gradually to advance over the river.

Presently, to my great joy, I saw it touch the other side, and at length become fixed and firm by its own weight. In a moment Fritz and Jack leaped upon the timber, and, in spite of my paternal fears, crossed the stream with a joyful step upon this narrow but effective bridge.

The first timber being thus laid, the difficulty of our undertaking was considerably diminished; a second and a third were fixed in succession, and with the greatest ease. Fritz and I, standing on opposite sides of the river, placed them at such distance from each other as was necessary for forming a broad and handsome bridge. What now remained to be done was to lay some short planks across them quite close to each other, which we executed so expeditiously that our whole undertaking was completed in a much shorter time than I should have imagined possible.

Our labour, however, had occasioned us so much fatigue, that we found ourselves unable for that day to enter upon new exertions, and the evening beginning to set in, we returned to our home, where we partook heartily of supper and went to bed.

As soon as we were all up and had breakfasted the next morning, I assembled all the members of my family together, to take with them a solemn farewell of this our first place of reception from the horrible disaster of the shipwreck.

I directed my sons to assemble our whole flock of animals, and to leave the ass and the cow to me, that I might load them with the sacks as we had planned. I had filled these at the two ends, and made a slit longways in the middle of each of them, and to each side of the slit I tied several long pieces of cord, which crossing each other and being again brought round and fastened, served to hold sacks firmly on the back of the animal. We next began to put together all the things we should stand most in need of, for the two or three first days, in our new abode; working implements, kitchen utensils, the captain's service of plate, and a small provision of butter, &c. I next added our hammocks and other coverings to complete the load, and we were about to begin our march when my wife stopped me.

"I cannot prevail upon myself," said she, "to leave our fowls behind us to pass the night by themselves, for I fear they would infallibly become the prey of jackals. We must somehow or other contrive a place for them among the luggage, and also one for our little Francis, who cannot walk so far, and on that account would not fail to interrupt our speed."

Fortunately I had already thought of making the ass's load as light as possible, foreseeing that it would be necessary he should carry our little one a part of the way. I now accordingly placed the child upon his back, fixing a bag in such a way as to support him; and I tied them together upon the ass with so many cords, that the animal might even have galloped without any danger of his falling off.

In the meanwhile the other boys had been running after the cocks and hens and the pigeons, but had not succeeded in catching one of them, so they returned empty-handed and in ill-humour. "Well," said their mother, "see how you have heated yourselves in running after the fowls. I could have put you in a way to catch them in a moment. Come along with me, and see."

"Yes, yes, you may think so, Mother," said Jack, a little sulky, "but I will give you leave to roast me in the place of the first fowl that you shall be able to catch."

"Poor Jack!" said his mother laughing, "you will then soon be on the spit, I can tell you; which would really be a pity, considering what better things we might do with you. To say truth, though, you have not shown that you have more brains than a goose, in thinking to catch the animals by running after them in this manner."

She now stepped into the tent, and brought out two handfuls of peas and oats, and calling to the birds in her accustomed tones, they flocked round her in a moment. She then walked slowly before them, dropping the grain all the way, till they had followed her into the tent. When they were all in the inside, and busily employed in picking up the grain, she shut the entrance, and caught one after the other, without the smallest difficulty. The boys looked at each other half-ashamed, though much amused with the adventure.

"Grant me a reprieve from the spit, Mother," cried Jack, "and I will do all I can to help you in securing your prisoners."

Accordingly he set himself to work, and had soon caught the whole of the fowls. They were then tied by the feet and wings, put into a basket covered with a net, and placed in triumph on the top of our luggage.

We packed up everything we were obliged to leave and placed it in the tent, which we carefully closed, and for greater security fastened down the ends of the sail-cloth at the entrance by driving stakes through them into the ground. We ranged a number of vessels, both full and empty, round the tent to serve as a rampart, and thus we confided to the protection of Heaven our remaining treasures. At length we set ourselves in motion. Every one of us carried a gun upon his shoulder and a game-bag at his back.

We had reached our bridge and advanced halfway across it, when the sow for the first time took the fancy of joining us, and, by the uncouth and listless figure she made, contributed to the pictorial effect of our procession.

On the other side of the river we experienced an inconvenience wholly unexpected. The nutritious aspect of the grass, which grew here in profusion, was too strong a temptation for our animals, who, unable to resist, strayed from us in every direction to feed upon it, so that, without the assistance of our dogs, we should not have been able to bring them back to the line of our procession. The dogs, indeed, were of great use to us on this occasion, and when everything was restored to proper order we were able to continue our journey. For fear, however, of a similar occurrence, I directed our march to the left, along the seaside, where there was not a sufficient quantity of grass to attract the animals.

Fritz had run on before with his gun. We followed him at our leisure, till at last, without further accident or adventure, we arrived at the place of the giant trees. Such, indeed, we found them, and our astonishment exceeded all description.

We began now to release our animals from their burdens, having first thrown our own on the grass. We next used the precaution of tying their two fore-legs together with a cord, that they might not go far away, or lose themselves. We restored the fowls to liberty and then, seating ourselves upon the grass, held a family council on the subject of our future establishment. I was myself somewhat uneasy on the question of our safety during the ensuing night, for I was ignorant of the nature of the country around us, and of what chance there might be of our being attacked by different kinds of wild beasts. I accordingly observed to my wife, that I would make an endeavour for us all to sleep in the trees that very night. While I was deliberating with her on the subject, Fritz, who thought of nothing but his sporting, had stolen away to a short distance, and we heard the report of a gun. This would have alarmed me, if at the same moment we had not recognized Fritz's voice crying out, "Hit! hit!" and in a moment we saw him running towards us, dragging a dead animal of uncommon beauty by the paws. "Father, Father, look! Here is a superb tiger-cat!" said he, proudly raising it off the ground to show it to the best advantage.

"Bravo! bravo!" cried I; "Your achievements will call forth the unbounded gratitude of our cocks and hens and pigeons, for you have rendered them what no doubt they will think an important service. If you had not killed this animal, he would no doubt have destroyed in the course of one night our whole stock of poultry."

Little Francis presently came running loaded with dry branches for his mother, his mouth crammed full of something, and calling out, "Mamma, Mamma, I have found a nice fruit to eat, and I have brought you home some of it!"

His mother, quite alarmed, made him open his mouth, and took out with her finger what he was eating with so keen a relish. With some difficulty she drew out the remains of a fig.

"A fig!" exclaimed I. "Where did you find it? Thank God, this is no poison! But nevertheless remember, Francis, that you are never to put anything in your mouth without first showing it to your mother or to me. And tell us where you got this fig."

"I got it among the grass, Father, and there are a great many more. I thought it must be good to eat, for the fowls and the pigeons, and even the pig, came to the place and ate them."

"You see, then, my dear," said I to my wife, "that our beautiful trees are fig-trees, at least the kind which are thus named at the Antilles, though they do not in the least resemble the tree called by that name in Europe, except that they both bear a fruit having some little resemblance to the European fig.

In the meanwhile my wife had been employed in making a fire, in putting on the pot, and preparing for our dinner.

Our repast being ended, I observed to my wife that I did not think it would be possible for us to sleep that night in the tree. I however, desired her immediately to begin preparing the harness for the animals, that they might go to the sea-shore and fetch the pieces of wood and such articles as I might find necessary for enabling us to ascend the tree, if, contrary to my expectation, it should be found practicable. She lost not a moment in beginning her work. In the meantime I set about suspending our hammocks to some of the arched roots of the trees, which I considered would give us a more comfortable resting place than the bare ground.

Having thus made the best provision I could for the night, I hastened with the two eldest boys to the sea-shore to examine what pieces of wood might have been thrown up by the waves, and to choose out such as were most proper for the steps of my ladder.

There were, no doubt, on the sands, numberless pieces, the quality of which was fit for my object. Unfortunately, however, there was none that would not require considerable labour to be adapted to my purpose, and thus my undertaking would have experienced a considerable delay, if Ernest had not been lucky enough to discover a number of bamboo-canes in a sort of bog, where they lay half covered with sand and mud. I took them out, and with the boys' assistance completely cleared them from the dirt, and stripped off their leaves to examine them, I found to my great joy that they were precisely what I wanted. I then instantly began to cut them with my hatchet in pieces of four or five feet long; the boys bound them together in faggots proportioned to their strength for carrying them, and we prepared to return with them to our place of abode. I next secured some of the straight and most slender of the stalks to make some arrows with, of which I knew I should stand in need. At some distance from the place where we stood I perceived a sort of thicket, in which I hoped I might find some young twigs, which I thought might also be useful to me. We had hardly reached the thicket when a troop of large-sized flamingoes sprang out, and with a loud rustling noise mounted into the air. Fritz, always too ready with his gun, instantly fired, when two of the birds fell down among the bushes. One of them was quite dead, but the other, slightly wounded in the wing soon got up, and giving himself a shake, and finding that he could not fly, began to make use of his long legs, and to run so fast towards the water, that we were afraid he would escape us. Fritz, in the joy in his heart, ran to pick up the flamingo he had killed. He plunged up to his knees in the water, and with great difficulty was able to get out again. Warned by his example, I proceeded more cautiously in my pursuit of the wounded bird. Ponto came to my assistance, and without him I should have lost all trace of the animal; but Ponto ran on before, caught hold of the flamingo, and held him fast till I reached the spot and took him into my protection. All this was effected with care for the bird made a stout resistance, flapping his wings with violence for some time.

The joy of the boys was excessive when they saw that my flamingo was alive. "If we can but cure his wound and contrive to feed him, what a happiness it will be!" said they. "Do you think that he will like to be with the other fowls?"

"I know," answered I, "that he is a bird that may be easily tamed, and we will make our experiment upon him."

We were now returned to the spot where we had left the three bundles of bamboo-canes, and as my sons were sufficiently loaded, I took charge of them myself.

We were at length arrived once more at our giant trees, and were received with a thousand expressions of interest and kindness. All were delighted at the sight of our new conquest.

I now began to examine his wound, and found that only one wing was injured by the ball, but that the other had also been slightly wounded by the dog's laying hold of him. I anointed them both with an ointment I composed of a mixture of butter and wine for the purpose, and which seemed immediately to ease the pain. I next tied him by one of his legs with a long string to a stake I had driven into the ground, quite near to the stream, that he might go in and wash himself when he pleased.

I now set Fritz and Ernest to work to measure our stock of thick ropes, of which I wanted no less than some eighty feet for the two sides of the ladder; the two youngest I employed in collecting all the small string we had used for measuring, and carrying it to their mother. For my own part, I sat down on the grass and began to make some arrows with a piece of the bamboo and the short, sharp points of the canes I had taken such pains to secure. As the arrows were hollow, I filled them with moist sand to give them a little weight, and lastly I tipped them with a bit of feather from the flamingo to make them fly straight. Scarcely had I finished my work than the boys came jumping round me, uttering a thousand demonstrations of joy.

"A bow! a bow! and some real arrows!" cried they, addressing each other and then running to me. "Tell us, Father," continued they, "what you are going to do with them? Do let me shoot one!"

"Have patience, boys; I say, have patience."

"Have you, my dear, any strong thread?" said I to my wife. "I want some immediately."

"Here is a whole ball of thread," she replied.

I now tied the end of the ball of strong thread to an arrow, and fixing it to the bow, I shot it off in such a direction as to make the arrow pass over one of the largest branches of the tree, and fall again to the ground on the other side. By this method I lodged my thread across the main branch, while I had the command of the end and the ball below. It was now easy to tie a piece of rope to the end of the thread, and draw it upwards till the knot should reach the same branch. We were thus enabled to measure the height it was from the ground, and it proved to be forty feet. Having now made quite sure of being able to raise my ladder by means of the string already suspended, we all set to work with increased zeal and confidence. The first thing I did was to cut a length of about a hundred feet from my parcel of ropes an inch thick; this I divided into equal parts, which I stretched along on the ground in two parallel lines, at the distance of a foot from each other. I then directed Fritz to cut pieces of bamboo-cane, each two feet in length. Ernest handed them to me, one after another; and as I received them inserted them into my cords at the distance of twelve inches respectively, fixing them with knots in the cord, while Jack, by my order, drove into each a long nail at the two extremities to hinder them from slipping out again. Thus in a very short time I had formed a ladder of forty rounds in length, and in point of execution firm and compact. We all beheld it with a sort of joyful astonishment. I now proceeded to fasten it firmly to one end of the rope which hung from the tree, and pulled it by the other till one end of our ladder reached the branch, and seemed to rest so well upon it that the joyous exclamations of the boys and my wife resounded from all sides. All the boys wished to be the first to ascend upon it, but I decided that it should be Jack, he being the nimblest and of the lightest figure among them. Accordingly the rest of us held the end of the rope with all our strength, while our young adventurer tripped up the ladder with as much ease as if he were a cat, and presently took his post upon the branch; but I observed that he had not strength enough to tie the rope firmly to the tree. Fritz now assured me that he could ascend the ladder as safely as his brother; but, as he was much heavier, I was not altogether without apprehension. I gave him instructions how to step in such a way as to divide his weight, by occupying four rounds of the ladder at the same time with his feet and hands. I made him take with him some large nails and a hammer, to nail the ladder firmly to the branch. He set out courageously upon the undertaking, and was almost instantly side by side with Jack, forty feet above our heads, and both saluting us with cries of exultation. Fritz immediately set to work to fasten the ladder by passing the rope round and round the branch, and this he performed with so much skill and intelligence, that I felt sufficient reliance to determine me to ascend myself, and well conclude the business he had begun. But before I ascended I tied a large pulley to the end of the rope, and carried it with me. When I was at the top I fastened the pulley to a branch which was within my reach, that by this means I might be able the next day to draw up the planks and timbers I might want for building my aerial castle. I executed all this by the light of the moon, and felt the satisfaction of having done a good day's work. I now gently descended my rope-ladder, and joined my wife.

At last we had notice that our supper was served. We had laid together in different heaps a quantity of dried branches and pieces of wood in readiness to light up, when my wife summoned us to our meal, which we had waited for with impatience, and now greedily devoured.

The children brought us some figs for the dessert, which they had picked up under the trees, and of which we all partook with pleasure. And now the gaping of one of the boys, and the outstretched arms of another, gave us notice that it was time for our young labourers to retire to rest. We performed our evening devotions. I set fire to several of the heaps, and then threw myself contentedly upon my hammock.

## CHAPTER V

I had thought it necessary to keep watch during this first night for the protection of my family. Every leaf that stirred gave me the apprehension that it was the approach of a jackal or a tiger, who might attack some member of my family. As soon as one of the heaps was consumed I lighted another. At length, finding that no animal appeared, I by degrees became assured, and at last fell into so sound a sleep that I did not awake early enough for the execution of my project of that day. The boys were all up and about me. We took our breakfast and fell to our work. My wife, having finished her daily occupation of milking the cow and preparing the breakfast for the family and for all the animals, set off with Ernest, Jack and Francis, attended by the ass, to the sea-shore. They had no doubt of finding some more pieces of wood, and they thought it would be prudent to replenish our exhausted store. In her absence I ascended the tree with Fritz, and made the necessary preparations for my undertaking, for which I found the tree in every respect convenient. The branches grew extremely close to each other, and in an exactly horizontal direction. Such as grew in a manner to obstruct my design, I cut off either with the saw or hatchet, leaving none but what presented me with a sort of foundation for my work. I left those which spread themselves evenly away from the trunk, and had the largest circuit, as a support for my floor. Above these, at the height of forty-six feet, I found others upon which to suspend our hammocks; and higher still there was a further series of branches, destined to receive the roof of our tent, which for the present was to be formed of nothing more than a large surface of sail-cloth.

The progress of these preparations was slow. It was necessary to hoist up to this height of forty feet beams that were too heavy for my wife and her little assistants to raise from the ground without great effort. I had, however, the resource of my pulley, which served to excellent purpose. My wife and her little boys fastened the beams to pieces of cord, while Fritz and I contrived to draw them up to the elevation of the tent one by one. When I had already placed two beams upon the branches, I hastened to fix my planks upon them. I made the floor double, that it might have sufficient solidity if the beams should be in any way warped from their places. I then formed a wall something like a park-paling all round, to prevent accidents to ourselves or children. This operation, and a third journey to the sea-shore to collect the timber necessary, filled our morning so completely that not one of us had thought about dinner. For this once it was requisite to be content with a simple provision of ham and milk. Dinner ended, we returned to work to finish our aerial palace, which now began to make an imposing appearance. We unhooked our hammocks from the projecting roots from which they had at first been suspended, and by means of the pulley hoisted them up to our new habitation. The sail-cloth roof was supported by the thick branches above. As it was of great compass, and hung down on every side, the idea occurred to me of nailing it to the paling on two sides, and thus getting not only a roof, but two walls also; the immense trunk of the tree forming a third side, while the fourth side contained the entrance of our apartment. This I left entirely open, both as a means of seeing what passed without and as a means of admitting a current of air. We also on this side enjoyed an extensive and uninterrupted view of the vast ocean and its lengthening shore. The hammocks were soon suspended from the branches above, and now everything was ready for our reception that very evening. Well satisfied with the execution of my plan I descended with Fritz, who had assisted me through the whole. As the day was not far advanced, and I observed we had still some planks remaining, we set about contriving a large table to be placed between the roots of the trees, and surrounded with benches; and this place, we said, should be called our dining-parlour. This time we performed our task but slightly, for I confess I was much fatigued. The table, on the whole, was, however, such as might be well endured, and the view of it gave my wife much satisfaction. In the meantime the three youngest boys collected all the pieces of wood we had thrown down from the tree, and put them together to dry in a heap at a small distance from our fireplace. I also tied together a quantity of small wood which we had collected, and which served to augment our store for making fires.

Entirely exhausted by the fatigues of the day, I threw myself at full length on a bank, saying to my wife that as I had worked like a galley-slave today, I should allow myself some rest tomorrow.

My wife answered, that not only was I entitled to a day of rest, but that it was a duty incumbent on me to take it on the following day. "For," said she, "I have calculated that tomorrow is Sunday."

Unfortunately we had already passed one Sabbath day without recollecting that it was so.

"I thank you, my dear," said I, "for making this discovery, and I promise you that the day shall be celebrated by us as it ought to be. Now that we seem to have surmounted many difficulties, and to have secured ourselves an habitation, we should indeed be culpable not to celebrate in a solemn and particular manner the day He has consecrated to Himself."

On waking in the morning, we were all sensible of an unusual refreshment, and a new activity of mind.

"Well, young ones," cried I jocosely, "you have learned, I see, how to sleep in a hammock. I heard not a single complaint all the night! No disputing about room from any one of you; all has still and tranquil."

"Yes, yes, Father, that is very true," said they, "so let us go to work again today. What is there to do? What will you give each of us to do?"

"Nothing at all, my children. You will not do any hard work with your hands for the whole day."

"Oh, Father, you are joking now, I see you are; you are laughing at us because we slept a little too long."

"No, my dear boys, I am not joking. This day is Sunday, and God said *six days shalt thou labour, but the seventh is the Sabbath of the Lord Thy God;* and we will therefore celebrate it as we ought, and refrain from all serious labour. Now let us descend to breakfast, and see to our animals."

Accordingly, after saying our prayers, we descended the ladder, and breakfasted on warm milk.

We served the animals also with their food, and then we all sat down on the tender grass, the boys full of impatient curiosity, their mother absorbed in silent reflexion.

All now standing up, I repeated aloud the church service, which I knew by heart, and we sung some verses from the hundred-and-nineteenth psalm, which the boys had before learned.

My wife then brought from her enchanted bag a copy of the Holy Bible, which, most thoughtful of women, she had brought with her from the wreck. I opened the book and read some passages from it to my family. In this solitude, in which for so long a time we had heard only our own thoughts expressed in vulgar enough language we were singularly affected with the words of Scripture. We felt forcibly that, notwithstanding our exile, we were still connected with the community of mankind.

My young folks remained for a time thoughtful and serious but by-and-by the gaiety natural to their ages prevailed, and each slipped away to seek the reaction he liked best.

Jack desired me to lend him my bow and arrows, as he wished to see how they would fly. Little Francis laid my activity under contribution, by requesting me to make him a bow and arrows, he being yet too young to be entrusted with a gun.

Our provision of powder must at last be exhausted; we might even at any moment be deprived of it by accident. It therefore was of the utmost importance to us to acquire some other means of killing animals, or of defending ourselves against enemies. The Caribees, I recollected, were taught at a very tender age to strike an object at the distance of thirty or forty steps; they hit the smallest birds perched on the top of the tallest trees. Why then should it not be possible for my boys to learn to do the same? "I will at least," said I, "provide them with bows and arrows, and try what can be done."

Jack had finished the trial of his arrows: they flew to admiration, and he practised his new art incessantly. Little Francis waited with impatience for the moment when he should do the same, and followed with his eyes everything I did. When I had finished my bow, and prepared some little arrows for him, I must next undertake to make him a quiver; "for," said he, "an archer can no more be without a quiver than a sportsman without a game-bag."

He put his arrows into it, and, happy as a chevalier in full armour, took his bow in his hand and ran to try his skill by the side of his brother. Fritz had also cleaned and prepared his materials when his mother summoned us to dinner. We cheerfully placed ourselves under the shade of our tree, round the table I had manufactured. At the end of the repast, I made the following proposition to the boys, which I was sure would give them pleasure.

"What think you, my good friends," said I, "of giving a name to the place of our abode, and to the different parts of the country which are known to us? I do not mean a general name to the whole island, for who knows but that some traveller may have already bestowed on it the name either of a great navigator or of some saint, and that our island may not already make a figure in the maps? But this need not prevent us from giving names to the objects we are concerned with, and which will make us better understand each other when we are conversing with them."

They all exclaimed joyfully that the idea was excellent.

## CHAPTER VI

In this pleasing kind of chat the time of dinner passed agreeably away. We settled the basis of a geography of our own country, and amused ourselves with saying that it must go by the first post to Europe.

During our talk, Ernest and Francis had exercised themselves in shooting their arrows. The evening was advancing, and the intense heat of the day began to diminish. I invited all my family to take a walk. "Leave your work for this time, my boys," said I, "and let us make a short excursion. Where shall we go?"

Fritz: "Let us go to Tent House, Father. We are in want of powder and shot."

My Wife: "I too vote for Tent House. My butter is nearly gone, for Fritz took an unreasonable share for his new trade of tanning."

Ernest: "If we go to Tent House, let us try to bring away some of the geese and ducks with us: they will look very well swimming about in our stream here, by Falcon's Nest."

Jack: "I will undertake to catch them if anyone will help to bring them home."

Father: "To Tent House, then, we will go. But we will not take our accustomed road along the seashore, but rather vary our pleasure by trying to explore some other way. We will keep along our own little stream as far as the wall of rocks, whose agreeable shade will accompany us almost as far as the cascade formed by Jackal's River. It will, I hope, as we have no burden to carry, be easy for us to cross it by jumping from stone to stone, and so get to Tent House. We will return with our provisions by the road of Family Bridge, and along the sea-shore; the sun, if not gone down, will then be at our backs."

Our route at first lay along the stream, sheltered by the shade of large trees. To prolong the pleasure of our walk we proceeded slowly, amusing ourselves with looking about us to the right and left. The eldest boys made frequent escapes, running on before so that we sometimes lost sight of them. In this manner we reached the end of the wood. The country now appearing to be less open, we thought it would be prudent to bring our whole company together. On looking forward we saw the boys approaching us full gallop, and this time, for a wonder, the grave Ernest was first. He reached me panting for breath, and so full of joy and eagerness that he could not pronounce a single word distinctly. He held out his hand, which contained three little balls of a light green colour.

"We have found a prize, Father!" cried he at last when he had recovered his voice. "We have found some potato-seed!"

I scarcely dared believe in so happy an event at the discovery of a plant which would place us for ever beyond the reach of hunger, and even of apprehension.

Ernest explained where he had found the plants, and we all hastened to the place where he had seen the tubers. With extreme joy we found there a large plantation of potato plants. A part of them were covered with their lilac and yellow blossoms, the sight of which conveyed more pleasure to our hearts than if they had been the most fragrant roses. Another portion of the plantation was in seed. And in several places some younger plants were pushing through the earth.

With our knives and sticks we soon procured a sufficient number to fill our bags and our pockets. When we were well loaded we again began to think of our walk to Tent House. Some of our company raised their voices in favour of returning immediately to Falcon's Stream to unload our cargo and prepare our booty for a delicious meal. But so many pressing motives presented themselves for proceeding to our store-house, that it was decided we should continue our route, which we accordingly resumed.

Presently we reached the long chain of rocks, over which our pretty Falcon's Stream made its escape in the form of a cascade. We kept along the chain of rocks which led to Jackal's River, and from thence to Tent House, having first with difficulty pushed through the high grass which presented itself in our path. We saw many specimens of the Indian fig, with its large broad leaf; aloes of different forms and colours; the superb prickly candle or cactus, bearing straight stalks, taller than a man, and crowned with long straight branches, forming a sort of star. The broad plantain spread along the rocks its innumerable boughs twisted with each other, hanging down perpendicularly, and ornamented with flowers, which grew in large tufts, and were of the brightest rose colour; while that which pleased us best, and which was found there in great abundance, was the king of fruits, both for figure and relish, the crowned pineapple. We immediately fell on this fruit with avidity, because we knew its value and its innocence, and because it was fit to be eaten without any further preparation than merely gathering it. The monkey was not the last to seize one for himself; and as he could make higher jumps than the boys, they formed the scheme of making him angry by little tricks, so as to induce him to fling pineapples at them. This game continued so long that I thought it prudent to interrupt them, fearing that the unripe state of the fruit might affect their health.

Soon after, I was fortunate enough to discover, among the multitude of plants which grew either at the foot or in the clefts of the rock, the karata, many of which were now in blossom, and of others the flowers had lately fallen off. Travellers have given so perfect a description of them in their books of natural history that it was impossible I should mistake them. But what further confirmed their identity was their straight slender stalk, crowned with blossoms, and proceeding from a tuft of leaves like the pineapple, with its large foliage terminating in a sharp point, and forming altogether a plant remarkably pleasing to the eye. As I was acquainted with the properties of this useful plant, the pith of which is used as tinder by the negroes, who also make a strong kind of thread from the fibres of its leaves, I was not less satisfied with my discovery than I had been with that of the potatoes. I did not hesitate to assure the boys that I preferred it to the pineapples.

All answered me, their mouths at the same time full of the fruit, that they would resign these trees with all their flowers to me if I would leave them the pineapples.

"The pineapples are better than all the rest," said they, "even than the potatoes. What is a handsome-looking tree worth if it does not bear any fruit?"

For answer I called to Ernest.

"Here," said I, "take out my flint and steel and strike me a light."

Ernest: "But, Father, what am I to do for tinder? What can I put to receive the sparks?"

Father: "This is precisely to the purpose. When the tinder which we brought from the vessel is all consumed, how shall we be able to make a fire? And without a fire how shall we dress a dinner, or prepare numberless other matters we have occasion for?"

Ernest: "Oh, I should not be in the least at a loss. We would do like the savages — rub two pieces of wood against each other till at length they catch fire."

Father: "Many thanks for the suggestion. But I think I can show you a better way."

I then took a dried stalk of the tree, stripped off the bark, and disclosed a dry spongy pith, which I laid upon the flint. Striking a spark with a steel, the pith instantly caught fire. The boys looked on with astonishment, and then began to caper about, exclaiming, "Long live the tinder-tree!"

"Here, then," said I, "we have an article of greater usefulness than if it served merely to gratify the appetite; your mother will next inform us what materials she will use for sewing your clothes when her provision of thread is exhausted."

My Wife: "I have long been uneasy upon this very subject, and would willingly give all the pineapples in the world in exchange for hemp or flax."

"And your wish shall be accomplished," said I. "For once I shall have the pleasure of presenting you with something you eagerly desire to have. If you examine, you will find some excellent thread under the leaves of this extraordinary plant, where all-provident nature has placed a store-house of this valuable article, though the lengths of thread will be found not longer than the leaf." I accordingly examined one of the leaves, and drew out of it a strong piece of thread of a red colour, which I gave to my wife. "We shall put the leaves to dry," said I, "either in the sun, or by a gentle fire. The useless part of the leaf will then separate by being beaten, and the mass of thread will remain."

Conversing thus, we reached Jackal's River, which we crossed, stepping with great care form stone to stone, and very shortly after arrived at our old habitation, where we found everything in perfect order as we had left it. We immediately dispersed, each on quest of what he intended to take away. Fritz loaded himself with powder and shot. My wife and I and Francis employed ourselves in filling our pot with butter, and the carrying of it on our return it was agreed was to fall on me. Ernest and Jack looked about for the geese and ducks, but as they were become somewhat wild, the boys did not succeed in catching one of them. The idea then occurred to Ernest of taking a small bit of cheese and tying it to the end of a piece of string, and holding it to float in the water. The voracious animals hastened eagerly to seize it. In this way, Ernest drew them towards him, one by one, with the cheese in its mouth, till he had caught the whole. We tied their legs together and fastened them to our game-bags, so that each had his share in carrying them.

We had thought of taking back with us a stock of salt, but we could not carry so much as we wished, the sacks being occupied with potatoes. I, however, thought of throwing a certain quantity loose into one of the sacks to fill up the space between the potatoes. In this way we secured a tolerable supply, but it made the sack so heavy that no one was willing to be encumbered with it. Fritz proposed that our faithful Turk should carry it; and accordingly the sack was tied on the back of the quiet, kind-tempered animal. Ponto was to carry the monkey as before.

We set out on our return, loaded with treasures, and the appearance of our caravan was even more amusing than it had been before. The ducks and geese, with their heads and necks stretching out at our shoulders, cackling with all their might, gave us a truly singular and ludicrous appearance. We could not help laughing immoderately as we passed the bridge, one after the other, loaded in so strange a fashion. Our jokes, and the general good-humour which prevailed, served to shorten the length of the walk, and we none of us were sensible of fatigue till we were seated under our tree at Falcon's Stream. My wife now prepared to put some of the potatoes, which we so eagerly desired to taste, immediately on the fire. She next milked the cow and the goat, and refreshed us with a draught of their warm milk. After dining heartily on our potatoes, on which we bestowed abundance of commendation, we concluded the day with evening prayers, and then joyfully climbed our ladder to seek the blessing of repose in our aerial castle.

## CHAPTER VII

I had remarked the evening before, on our return to the sea-shore, a quantity of wood, of which I thought I could make a king of conveyance for our cask of butter and other provisions from Tent House to Falcon's Stream. I had secretly determined to go early the next morning, before my family should be awake, to the spot. I had fixed upon Ernest for my assistant, thinking that his indolent temper required to be stimulated to exertion. He felt as a great favour the preference I gave him, and he promised to be ready at a very early hour. I was also desirous to leave Fritz with the family, as, being the tallest and strongest, he was more able to protect the rest.

As soon as I perceived the first dawn of morning I quietly awoke Ernest. He raised himself, stretching and gaping in his hammock. We descended the ladder without being perceived by the rest of the family, who continued to sleep soundly. The first thing we had to do was to loose the ass, who was to be of our party. That he might not go without a load, I made him draw a very large branch of a tree, which I wanted for my undertaking.

As we walked along, I asked Ernest if he was not a little out of humour at being obliged to get up so early, to set about a laborious occupation, instead of remaining with his brothers to shoot at the thrushes and the pigeons on the fig-tree.

"Not in the least, Father," said Ernest; "now I am once up and dressed, I do not mind it at all. I like being with you, and assisting you, very much."

When we reached the sea-shore we found the pieces of wood in great abundance. I determined to cut such pieces as I wanted of the proper length, and to lay them cross-ways on the branches which the ass had drawn to the place, and by this means to make them serve as a kind of sledge. We lost no time in setting to work, and we added to the load a little chest which we found half-buried in the sands, quite close to the waves. We also provided ourselves with some poles which lay there, that we might use them as rollers, should we stand in need of them for passing difficult places, and then we set out on our return to Falcon's Stream. When we were within a certain distance of our abode we heard a loud firing, which informed us that the attack upon the ortolans was in good train. On seeing us approach, the cries of joy which were uttered resounded in every direction, and all ran eagerly to meet us. The chest we had brought was soon opened by a strong hatchet, for all were eager to see what was within. It contained only some sailor's suits of clothes and some linen, which was quite wet with the sea.

I had to account to my wife for having absented myself with one of the boys without giving her notice or bidding her adieu. She had been uneasy, and I confessed I had been to blame.

I next inspected the booty of the three sportsmen, who had shot in all no less than fifty ortolans and thrushes. I taught them how to make some snares to be suspended from the fig-tree, and advised them to use the thread of the karata, which is as strong as horse-hair, for the purpose. What is new always amuses young persons, and the boys accordingly took a great fancy to this mode of sporting. Jack succeeded in his first attempt. I left Francis to assist him, and took Fritz and Ernest to help me in making the sledge. As we were all hard at work, for my wife had joined the youngest boys, we suddenly heard a prodigious clatter among the fowls; the cock crowed louder than all the rest together, and the hens ran to and fro as if they were pursued by a fox.

"I wonder what is the matter with the creatures," said my wife, rising. "Every day I hear the hens clucking as if they had been laying eggs."

At this moment Ernest happened to look at the monkey, and remarked that he fixed his piercing eyes on the hens. When he saw my wife approaching, driving the hens before her, the young rascal jumped quickly into a hollow place under one of the roots of the tree, and hid himself. Ernest ran to the place as soon as he, and was fortunate enough to seize him, seeing that he held a new-laid egg in his paw, which he was going to conceal in this place for future use. The monkey sprang immediately to such another hole, and Ernest followed. Here also he found some eggs, and brought them in his hat to his mother, who received them with great pleasure.

In the meanwhile Jack had got up into the tree, and had suspended some of the snares to the branches, to catch the little devourers of our figs. He came down again to bring us the acceptable intelligence that our pigeons, which we brought from the vessel, had made a sort of nest there of some dry grass, and that it already contained several eggs. I therefore forbade the boys to fire any more in the tree, for fear of alarming or wounding these gentle creatures. I also directed that the snares should be frequently examined, to see that the pigeons were not caught in them, as they might be strangled in their efforts to get loose. I should now even have forbidden the use of the snares, if I had not myself made them known to the boys, and that so very lately.

Meantime I was busily employed upon my sledge, which was soon completed; and I found that necessity had converted a preacher of moderate talents into a tolerably good carpenter. Two bent pieces of wood, the segments of a circle, formed the outline of my machine, which I fixed in their places by a straight piece of wood, placed across and firmly fixed to the bent pieces in the middle and at the rear. I then fastened two ropes to the front of my work, and my sledge was finished. As I had not raised my eyes from my work, I did not know what my wife and the two youngest boys had been about. On looking up, I perceived that they had been stripping off the feathers from a quantity of birds which the boys had killed, and that they afterwards spitted them on an officer's sword, that my wife had turned into a useful kitchen utensil. I approved of the idea, but I remarked on her profusion in dressing more birds at once than we could eat. She reminded me that I had myself advised her to half-roast the birds before putting them into the butter, to be preserved for future use. She was in hopes, she said, that as I had now a sledge, I should not fail of going to Tent House after dinner to fetch the cask of butter, and in the meanwhile she was endeavouring to be ready with the birds. I had no objection to this, and immediately determined on going to Tent House after dinner the same day, and requested my wife to hasten it for that purpose. She replied that this was already her intention, as she also had a little project in her head, which I should be informed of at my return. I, for my part, had one too, which was to take a bathe in the sea, and thus refresh myself from the heat and fatigue of my laborious occupations. I wished that Ernest, who was to accompany me, should bathe also; while Fritz was to remain at home for the protection of the family.

## CHAPTER VIII

As soon as Ernest and I had dined, we prepared for our departure.

We now set about harnessing the ass and cow to our sledge. Each of us took a piece of bamboo-cane in hand, to serve as a whip; and, resting our guns upon our shoulders, we began our journey. Ponto was to accompany us, and Turk to remain behind. We bade adieu to our companions and put our animals in motion. We took the road by the sea-shore, where the sands afforded better travelling for our vehicle than did the thick wild grass. We reached Family Bridge on Jackal's River, and arrived at Tent House without either obstacle or adventure. We immediately unharnessed the animals to let them graze, while we set to work to load the sledge with the cask of butter, the cask of cheese, a small barrel of gunpowder, different instruments, some ball and shot. These exertions had so occupied our thoughts that it was late when we first observed that our animals, attracted by the excellent quality of the grass on the other side of the river, had repassed the bridge, and wandered so far as to be out of sight. I was in hopes they would be easily found, and I directed Ernest to go with Ponto and bring them back, intending in the meantime to look for a convenient place on the other side of Tent House to have our bathe. In a short time I found myself at the extremity of Providence Bay, which ended, as I now perceived, in a marsh, producing the finest bulrushes it was possible to imagine. Farther on a chain of steep rocks advanced into the sea, forming a kind of creek, as if expressly contrived for bathing. The juttings of the rock even seemed like little separate cabinets, where one might be concealed from one's companions. Enchanted with this discovery, I called out to Ernest to come and join me, and in the meantime I amused myself with cutting some of the rushes, and imagining what use I could apply them to. Ernest neither replied nor came, so, after waiting a little, I resolved to go in pursuit of him, for I was unable to refrain from some uneasy sensations at his absence. Looking about in all directions, I at length discovered him at a distance, extended at his length on the ground, in the shade of Tent House. I approached him with a beating heart, fearing he might have been attacked by some wild beast, and was agreeably surprised at finding him in a sound and quiet sleep, while the ass and the cow were eating the grass close to the place where he lay.

"Come, come, young traveller, you must awake," cried I, shaking him. "While you are sleeping here, your animals may once more make their escape."

He instantly awoke starting, and was soon on his feet.

"Oh, but I defy them to escape across the bridge," said he, rubbing his eyes; "for I have taken away some of the planks, and left a space which they will have no great inclination to jump over."

Father: "Since your idle fit has rendered you inventive, I forgive it with all my heart. But is it not a pity to lose in sleeping the opportunity of doing something useful? Did you not promise your mother to carry her some salt? Slothfulness is always a fault where labour is a necessity."

Ernest: "But, Father, my head was not idle, I assure you. I was planning something all the time."

Father: "Really, Ernest! Pray tell me what important and profound study it was which made you go to sleep?"

Ernest: "I will tell you. I was thinking how difficult it would be to bring away from the vessel everything which it contains."

Father: "And did you hit upon some method for removing the difficulty?"

Ernest: "No, Father, no great things; I fell asleep in the middle of my reflections."

Father: "So this is the hard work your poor head was engaged in. Discovering a difficulty, and finding no means for conquering it!"

Ernest: "At this very moment an idea strikes me. We ought to have a large raft; but the beams of the ship are too heavy for the purpose. I think it would be better to take a number of the empty casks, and nail some planks upon them to keep them all together. I have read that the savages of America fill the skins of goats with air, tie them to each other, and are thus enabled to use them as rafts upon the largest rivers."

Father: "This is a sound idea, and one day or other we may perhaps derive advantage from it; but for the present, my boy, we must make up for lost time. Run, therefore, and fill this little bag with salt, which you will then empty into the large one that the ass is to carry, and which you will take care to fill equally on each side. During this time I will take the refreshment of bathing, and then it will be your turn to bathe and mine to take care of the animals."

I returned to the rocks, and was not disappointed in my expectation of an enjoyment the most delicious; but I did not stay long, fearing my boy might be impatient for his share of so new a pleasure. When I had dressed myself I returned to the place, to see if his work had advanced; but he was not there, and I supposed that he had again fallen asleep in some corner. Presently, however, I heard his voice calling out:

"Father, Father, a fish! A fish of monstrous size! Run quickly, Father, I can hardly hold him! He is eating up the string of my line!"

I ran to the place from which the voice proceeded, and found Ernest lying along the ground on his face, upon the extremity of a point of land, and pulling in his line, to which a large fish was hanging, and beating about with all his strength. I ran hastily and snatched the rod out of his hand, for I had some apprehension that the weight and activity of the fish would pull him into the water. I gave a certain liberty to the line, to calm the fish, and then contrived to draw him gently along till I had got him safely into a shallow, from which he could no longer escape, and thus the animal was effectually secured. We next examined him thoroughly, and it appeared to me that it could not weigh less than fifteen pounds; so that our capture was magnificent, and would afford the greatest pleasure to our good steward of provisions at Falcon's Stream.

"You have now really laboured," said I to Ernest, "not only with your head, but with your whole body, so I would advise you to wipe the perspiration from your face, and keep a little quiet before you venture into the water. You have procured us a dish of great excellence, which will last for several days, and have conducted yourself like a true chevalier, without fear and without reproach."

"It was at least fortunate," observed he in a modest tone, "that I thought of bringing my fishing-rod."

Father: "Certainly it was. But tell me how you came to see this large fish, and what made you think you could catch it?"

Ernest: "I used to remark when we lived at Tent House, that there were many fish in the water, just hereabouts. This made me determine to bring my fishing-tackle with me. On my way to the place where we keep the salt, I saw a geat number of little crabs, upon which fishes feed, near the water's brink. I thought I would try to bait my hook with one of them. So I hurried up my task of fetching the salt, and came to this spot, where at first I caught only some very little fish, which are there in my handkerchief. Then I remarked that these were chased in the water by fishes of larger size. This gave me the idea of baiting my hook with one of the small ones. I put a larger hook to my line, and in a short time the large fish you see there seized upon the bait, and paid his life for his voracity. However, I must confess that if you had not come to my assistance, I must either have let go my line or have been dragged into the water, for the fish was stronger than I."

We now examined the smaller fishes he had caught, which for the most part appeared to me to consist of little herrings, while I felt certain that the large one was a large cod. I immediately cut them all open, and rubbed them in the inside with salt, that they might not be injured by the heat. While I was thus employed Ernest went to the rocks and bathed, and I had time to fill some more bags with salt before his return. We then set about harnessing and loading our animals, after which we restored the planks which had been taken from the bridge, and then resumed the road to Falcon's Stream.

When we had proceeded about half-way, Ponto, who had been walking quietly on before us, suddenly escaped, and by his barking gave us notice that he scented some game. We soon after saw him pursuing an animal which seemed endeavouring to escape, and made the most extraordinary jumps imaginable. The dog continued to follow the creature in trying to avoid him passing within gunshot of the place where I stood. I fired, but its flight was so rapid that I missed. Ernest, who was at a small distance behind, hearing the report of my gun, prepared his own, and fired it off at the instant the singular animal was passing near him in pursuit of a hiding-place among the tall herbage just by. He aimed so well that the animal fell dead at the same instant. I ran hastily, and with extreme curiosity, to ascertain what kind of quadruped it was. We found it, in form and general appearance, the most remarkable possible to conceive. It was of the size of a sheep, with a tail resembling that of a tiger. Both its snout and hair were like those of a mouse, and its teeth were like a hare's, but much larger. The fore-legs resembled those of the squirrel, and were extremely short. But to make up for this, its hind-legs were very long. We examined the creature for a long time in silence. I could not be sure that I had ever seen an engraving of it in any Natural History, or a description of it in any book of travels. Ernest, after a long and close examination interrupted our silence by an exclamation of joy. "And have I really killed this extraordinary animal?" said he, clapping his hands together. "What will my mother and my brothers say? How astonished they will be! and how fortunate I am in securing so fine a prize! What do you think is its name, Father? I would give all the world to know."

"And so would I, my boy; but I am as ignorant as you. One thing, however, is certain, that this is your lucky day. For you have already performed two wonderful feats by destroying two monsters in the course of it, so that I shall be tempted to give you the name of my little Hercules. You also sometimes deserve that of my little Solomon. So let us both examine this interesting stranger with attention, that we may be certain to what family of quadrupeds it belongs. This will perhaps throw a light upon its name."

Ernest: "I think it can hardly be named a quadruped, for the little fore-legs look much more like hands, as is the case with monkeys."

Father: "They are notwithstanding legs, nevertheless, I can assure you. Let us look for its name among the mammalia. On this point we cannot be mistaken. Now let us examine its teeth."

Ernest: "Here are the four incisor teeth, like the squirrel."

Father: "Thus we see that it belongs to the order of Nibblers. Now let us look for some names of animals of this kind."

Ernest: "Besides the squirrels, I recollect only the mice, the marmots, the hares, the beavers, the porcupines, and the jumpers."

Father: "The jumpers! That word furnishes the necessary cluc; the animal is completely formed like the gerboa or jumping-hare, except that it is twice the size of those of which I have read a description... Wait a moment, an idea strikes me. I will lay a wager that our animal is one of the large jumpers, called kangaroo; it belongs properly to the genus Didelphis or Philander, because the female, who never bears more than one young one, carries it in a kind of purse placed between her hind-legs. To the best of my knowledge this animal has never been seen but on the coast of New Holland, where it was first observed by the celebrated navigator Captain Cook. You may then be highly flattered with your adventure in killing an animal at once so rare and so remarkable."

I now tied the fore-legs of the kangaroo together, and by means of two canes, we with considerable trouble contrived to carry it to the sledge, upon which it was securely fastened.

We at length arrived happily, though somewhat late, at Falcon's Stream, having heard from a great distance the kind welcome of the salutations of our family, and such a variety of questions asked, that

Ernest and I scarcely knew which to answer first. Fritz was the only one who was a little silent. I saw plainly by his countenance what was passing in his mind. He was jealous of the good fortune of his brother Ernest. But I also saw that he was struggling manfully against the ascendency of so mean a passion, and was resolving to conquer it. In a short time he had succeeded so completely that he joined frankly and unaffectedly in our conversation and merriment, and I am persuaded no one but myself perceived what was passing in his mind. He came near the kangaroo and examined it with great attention. Then, turning to his brother, he observed to him in a kind tone that he had had good luck, and that he must be a good shot to have killed the kangaroo with so little difficulty. "But, Father," said he, "when you go again to Tent House, or on any other excursion, will it not be my turn to go with you? For here at Falcon's Stream there is nothing new to amuse us; a few thrushes and some pigeons, this is all we have from day to day, and I find it very tiresome."

"I will promise you with all my heart what you desire, my dear boy," said I, "for you have valiantly combated the ill-humour and the jealousy which assailed your temper on witnessing your brother's success with the kangaroo. I therefore promise that you shall accompany me in my very next excursion, which will probably take place at no greater distance of time than tomorrow. It will be another journey to the vessel. But in the meantime, let me observe to you, my dear Fritz, that you ought to be more flattered with the high opinion I have shown of your prudence and judgement in leaving you here in charge of your mother and your brothers. You have accomplished an important duty in keeping near them all the time, and not suffering yourself to be allured by such amusements as presented themselves to your fancy. Praise is also due to Ernest for the moderation with which he has felt his triumph. He has not even told you of my humiliating failure in attempting to shoot the kangaroo."

We concluded the day with our ordinary occupations. I gave some salt to each of our animals, to whom it was an acceptable treat. We next skinned our kangaroo, and put it carefully aside until the next day, when we intended to cut it to pieces, and lay such parts in salt as we could not immediately consume. We made an excellent supper on our little fish, to which we added some potatoes; nor were our faithful companions, Turk and Ponto, neglected. The labours of the day had more than usually disposed us all to seek repose; we therefore said our prayers at an early hour mounted our ladder, and were soon asleep.

I rose with the first crowing of the cock, before the rest of the family were awake, descended the ladder, and employed myself in carefully skinning the kangaroo, so as not to deface its beautiful mouse-coloured coat. This gave me so much trouble, and I advanced so slowly in the business, that all my little family were assembled about me and their mother, and calling out "Famine!" before I had finished my work. Breakfast over, I ordered Fritz to prepare everything to go to Tent House, and prepare our boat, that we might proceed to the vessel.

We began our journey after having taken an affectionate leave of my wife and of my little Francis.

After having bid adieu we got into the boat, and we left the shore to gain the current of the stream. We quickly cleared Safety Bay, and reached the vessel, whose open side offered us an ample space to get up it. As soon as we had got on board and our boat was securely fastened, our first care was to look out for fit materials to construct a raft.

Our boat being built of staves had neither room nor solidity enough to carry a considerable burden. We therefore looked about, and soon found a sufficient number of water-casks, which appeared to me very proper for my intended new enterprise. We immediately emptied them, then replaced the bungs carefully, and threw the casks overboard, after securing them by means of ropes and cramps, so as to keep them together at the vessel's side. This completed, we placed a sufficient number of planks upon them to form a firm and commodious platform or deck, to which we added a gunwale of a foot in depth all round to secure the lading. Thus we contrived to possess a very handsome raft, in which we could stow thrice as much as in our boat. This laborious task had taken up the whole day. We scarcely allowed ourselves a minute to eat a mouthful of cold meat we had provided for the expedition, that we might not lose any time in looking for the provisions on board the vessel. In the evening Fritz and I were so weary that it would have been impossible for us to row back to land, even if our business had not detained us. We therefore came to the necessary resolution of passing the night on board; and having taken all due precautions in case of a storm, we reposed ourselves in the captain's cabin, on a good elastic mattress essentially different from our hammocks.

In fact, it so lulled us to rest and induced such sound repose, that our prudent design to watch in turn for fear of accident quite escaped us, and we both slept heavily side by side, till broad daylight opened our eyes, when we awoke with lively gratitude to that Providence to whom we were indebted for the quiet and comfortable night we had passed. We rose and actively set to work to load our raft.

In the first place, we completely stripped the cabin which had been occupied by my family on board the vessel, removing everything it contained which belonged to us previous to the fatal event of the wreck. Then we proceeded to the cabin in which we had slept so well, and carried off the very doors and windows, with their hinges. Some valuable chests of the officers were there; but this discovery and the rich lace clothes which seemed to court our grasp, were less acceptable to us than the carpenter's and gunner's chests, containing all their tolls and implements. Those which we could remove with levers and rollers were put entire upon the raft, and we took out of the others the things that made them too heavy. One of the captain's chests was filled with a number of costly articles, which no doubt he meant to dispose of to the opulent planters of Port Jackson, or among the savages. In the collection were several gold and silver watches, snuff-boxes of all descriptions, buckles, shirt-buttons, necklaces, and rings—in short, an abundance of all the trifles of European luxury. There was also a strong-box full of louis d'or and dollars, which attracted our notice less than another containing a very pretty table-service of fine steel, which we had substituted for the captain's, that were silver, and for which my wife had shown no small regard. But the discovery that delighted me most, and for which I would readily have given the box of louis d'or, &c., was a chest containing some dozens of young plants of every species of European fruits, which had been carefully packed in moss for transportation. I perceived pear, plum, almond, peach, apple, apricot, chestnut-trees, and vine-shoots. I beheld with a feeling I cannot describe those productions of my dear country, which once so agreeably embellished my rural dwelling, and which, if God vouchsafed to bless them, would thrive in a foreign soil. We discovered a number of bars of iron and large pigs of lead, grinding-stones, cartwheels ready for mounting, a complete set of farrier's instruments, tongs, shovels, ploughshares, rolls of iron and copper wire, sacks full of maize, pease, oats, vetches, and even a little hand-mill. The vessel had been freighted with everything likely to be useful in an infant colony so distant; nothing had been forgotten. We found a saw-mill in a separated state, but each piece numbered and so accurately fitted that nothing was easier than to put it together for use.

I had now to consider what of all these treasures I should take or leave. It was impossible to carry with us in one trip such a quantity of goods; and to leave them in the vessel, ready to fall to pieces and threatened every moment with complete destruction, was exposing ourselves to be wholly deprived of them, while every article so lost would be a subject of regret to us.

"Ah," said Fritz, "let us leave, in the first place, this useless money and the chest of trinkets, except the watches we promised my brothers, all the rest can be of no service to us."

"It gives me pleasure, my boy, to hear you speak thus of gold, that is the idol so universally adored. We will do, then, as you wish, and determine upon taking with us what is really useful, such as the powder, lead, iron, the corn and the fruit-trees, implements for gardening and agriculture. Let us take as many as possible of these last. If we should have any room left, we can then select a few of the objects of luxury. However, begin by taking from the chest the two watches I have promised, and one for yourself."

We then loaded our raft, not without difficulty and hard labour; we, moreover, stowed away a large and handsome fishing-net, quite new, and the vessel's great compass. With the net, Fritz found luckily two harpoons and a rope windlass, such as they use in the whale fishery. Fritz asked me to let him place the windlass, with the harpoons attached to the end of the rope, over the bow of the tub-boat, and thus hold all in readiness in case of seeing any large fish. As I thought it was unusual to meet with these so near the shore, I indulged him in his innocent fancy.

It was afternoon before we had finished our lading, for not only our raft was as full as it could hold, but our boat likewise.

Having well and completely executed our undertaking, both as to construction and lading, we stepped into the tub-boat, and with some small difficulty, which a little reflection and a few experiments soon enabled us to overcome, we pushed out for the current, drawing our raft triumphantly after us with a stout rope, which we had been careful to fasten securely at its head.

The wind was in a humour favourable to our undertaking, and briskly swelled our sail. The sea was calm, and we advanced without fear at a considerable rate. Fritz had been looking steadily for some time at something of a large size which was floating at some distance on the water, and he now desired me to take the glass and see what it could be. I soon perceived distinctly that it was a tortoise, which, agreeably to the habits of its singular species, had fallen asleep in the sun on the surface of the water, and we observed that it dit not in the least appear sensible of our approach. No sooner had Fritz learned this, than he earnestly entreated me to steer softly within view of so extraordinary a creature, that he might examine it at his ease. I readily consented. But as his back was towards me, and the sail was between us, I did not observe what he was about till I felt a violent jerk of the boat, a sudden turning of the windlass, accompanied by a rapid motion of the boat.

"Whatever are you about, Fritz?" exclaimed I. "Have you a mind to destroy us with your thoughtlessness?"

"I have caught him! — I touched him!" cried Fritz, without hearing one word I had been saying. "The tortoise is ours! It cannot escape, Father! Is not this, then, a valuable prize, for it will furnish dinners for us all for many weeks?"

I soon admitted the idea that in reality the harpoon had secured the animal, which, feeling itself wounded, thus agitated the vessel in its endeavours to be disengaged, for the rope of the harpoon was necessarily fastened at the other end to the windlass. I quickly pulled down the sail, and seizing a hatchet sprung to the boat's head to cut the rope and let the harpoon and the tortoise go; but Fritz caught hold of my arm, begging me to wait a moment, there being no immediate cause for alarm, and not so hastily bring upon him the mortification of losing, at one stroke, the harpoon, the rope, and the tortoise. He proposed watching himself with the hatchet in his hand to cut the rope suddenly should any sign of danger appear. I yielded to his entreaties, after a due exhortation to him to take good care not to upset the boat or run her upon the rocks.

Thus, then, drawn along by the tortoise, we proceeded with a hazardous rapidity, and having no small difficulty to keep the head of the boat in a straight direction, and keep her steady and prevent her yielding to the irregular motions of so singular a conductor. In a little time I observed that the creature was making for the sea. I therefore again hoisted the sail. As the wind was to the land, and very brisk, the tortoise found resistance of no avail. He accordingly fell into the track we desired to take, and we soon gained the current which had always received us in our visits to and from the wreck. He drew us straight towards our usual place of landing, and by good fortune without striking upon any of the rocks which so much abound in that spot. We, however, did not disembark without encountering one difficult adventure. I perceived that the state of the tide was such that we should be thrown upon one of the sand-banks, which indeed took place. We were at this time within a gunshot of the shore. The boat, though driven with violence, remained perfectly upright in the sand. I stepped into the water, which did not reach for above my knees, for the purpose of conferring upon our conductor his just reward for the alarm he had caused us, when he suddenly gave a plunge, and I saw him no more. Following the rope, I however soon found the tortoise stretched at length at the bottom of the water, where it was so shallow that I was not long in finding means to put an end to his pain. Being now near Tent House, Fritz gave a halloo and fired a gun, to apprise our relatives that we were not only arrived, but arrived in triumph. This soon produced the desired effect. The good mother and her three young ones soon appeared, running towards us.

After some gentle reproaches from my wife for leaving her and the boys for so long a time, the history of the tortoise was related in due form, and excited due interest and much merriment in our auditors. The tender-hearted mother began to shudder at the thought of the danger we had been exposed to, and the escape we had effected.

Our conversation being ended, I requested my wife to go with two of the younger boys to Falcon's Stream and fetch the sledge and the beasts of burden, that we might not fail of seeing at least a part of our booty from the ship put safely under shelter the same evening. A tempest, or even the tide, might sweep away the whole during the night. We took every precaution in our power against the latter danger by fixing the boat and the raft as securely as we could without an anchor. I rolled two heavy masses of lead, with the assistance of levers, from the raft upon the shore and then tied a rope to each, the other ends of which were fastened one to the raft and the other to the boat, and thus satisfied myself that they could not easily be forced away.

While we were employed on this scheme the sledge arrived, and we immediately placed the tortoise upon it, and also some other articles of light weight, such as mattresses, pieces of linen, &c. The strength of our whole party was found necessary to move it from the raft to the sledge, we therefore, all set out together to unload it again at Falcon's Stream. We pursued our way thither with the utmost gaiety of heart, and Fritz and I found the time pass both agreeably and quickly in answering the numerous questions with which the three youngest boys assailed us as to the nature and amount of the treasures we had brought from the vessel. The chest containing the articles in silver, and another filled with trinkets and utensils made of different kinds of metals, the most powerfully excited their interest; for Fritz had dropped a hint of what was in them, and nothing could exceed the measure of their curiosity.

In this trifling kind of talk we beguiled the time till we reached the foot of our castle. Our first concern now was the tortoise, which we immediately turned on his back that we might strip off the shell, and make use of some of the flesh while it was fresh. My wife expressed her fear that we should fail in our attempt. But taking my hatchet, I separated the upper and under shell all round, which were joined together by cartilages. The upper shell of the tortoise is extremely convex. The under, on the contrary, is nearly flat. Having succeeded in dividing them, I cut away as much of the flesh of the animal as was sufficient for a meal, and then laid the remaining mass carefully and neatly on the under shell, which served as a dish, recommending to my wife to cook what I had cut off on the other shell, with no other seasoning than a little salt, and pledged myself that she would by this means produce a most luxurious food.

"Oh", cried Francis, "do give me the shell, Father, it will be such a pretty plaything!"

"No, no!" bawled out another, and one and all contended for the preference.

I imposed silence, declaring that the right was entirely in Fritz, since it was he who had harpooned the animal, who, but for his dexterity and skill, would be at this moment existing in the sea. "But," continued I, "it may well be to ask what Fritz would think of doing with the shell."

"I thought, Father, of cleaning it thoroughly and fixing it by the side of our river, and keeping it always full of pure water for my mother's use when she has to wash the linen or cook our victuals."

"Excellent, excellent, my boy! All honour to the founder of the pure water-tub! This is what I call thinking for the general good. And we will take care to execute the idea as soon as we can prepare some clay as a solid foundation for its bottom."

By the time of ending this discourse we had also finished unloading the sledge, and I bade the three eldest boys accompany me to fetch another load before it should be dark. We left Francis and his mother busy in preparing what we indeed stood much in need of after a day of such fatigue, a refreshing meal for supper, the tortoise having presented itself most opportunely for this purpose.

"I promise you", cried my wife as we were moving off, "you shall not at your return find reason to complain."

As we walked along, Fritz asked me if this handsome shell was of the kind so much valued in Europe for making into boxes, combs, &c., and if it was not a pity to use it for a water-tub.

I replied that in our deserted situation the utility of a thing formed its greatest, and indeed only, value.

We now reached the raft, and took from it as many effects as the sledge could hold, or the animals draw along. The first object of my attention was to secure two chests which contained the clothes of my family, which I well knew would afford the highest gratification to my exemplary wife, who had frequently lamented that they were all compelled to wear clothes that were not their own, reminding her at every moment, she said, how much they might be wanted by their proper claimants. I reckoned also on finding in one of the chests some books, and principally a large handsomely-printed Bible. I added to these four cart-wheels and a hand-mill for grinding.

On our return to Falcon's Nest we found my wife looking anxiously for our arrival, and ready with the welcome she had promised, of an ample and agreeable repast. Nor was her kind humour diminished by the view of the acquisitions we now added to her store of necessaries.

Before she had well examined them, she drew me, with one of her sweetest smiles, by the arm. "Step this way", said she, "and I too will produce something that will both refresh and please you." And leading to the shade of a tree, "This", continued she, "is the work I performed in your absence," pointing to a cask of tolerable size half-sunk into the ground, and the rest covered over with branches of trees. She then applied a small corkscrew to the side, and filling the shell of a cocoa-nut with the contents, presented it to me. I found the liquor equal to the best Canary I had ever tasted.

"How then," said I, "have you performed this new miracle?"

"I took a little ramble in your absence yesterday to see what I could find, and behold how well my trouble was rewarded! The boys ran for the sledge, and had but little difficulty in getting it to Falcon's Stream, where our next care was to dig a place in the earth to receive and keep it cool. We guessed it must contain some sort of wine, but to be quite sure Ernest and Jack bored a small hole in the side, and inserting a hollow reed they contrived to taste it, and assured me the cask was filled with a most delicious beverage. I now thought it was high time to forbid their proceeding any further with the tasting, fearing for the effect on their poor heads. I closed up the hole with a small piece of wood. I have nothing more to relate, but that the boys kept the secret, as I desired them."

After supper I completed my day's work by drawing up the mattresses we had brought from the ship to our chamber in the tree by means of a pulley. When I had laid them along to advantage, they looked so inviting that I was glad the time had come to commit ourselves to the kind relief they offered to our exhausted strength.

## CHAPTER IX

I rose before day to go to the seaside and inspect our two vessels. My family did not hear me depart, and I was unwilling to disturb their balmy sleep, that sweet restorative of strength so requisite for children. I therefore gently descended the ladder. As I walked towards the shore, animated at different moments by hope and fear, with pleasure I saw there that, with the help of my lead and iron bars used as anchors, the boat and raft had resisted the tide. I got quickly on the raft, took a small loading, and returned to Falcon's Stream in time for breakfast. Judge of my surprise when arrived, that I neither saw nor heard a single creature of its inhabitants, though the sun had climbed high above the horizon. Thinking it time for our fellow-labourers to be stirring, I gave a shout as loud as a war-whoop. My wife awoke first, and wondered to see the day so far advanced.

"Really, my dear," said she, "I think it must be the magic charm of the good mattress you brought home yesterday that has lulled me into such a long, sound sleep, and that appears to be still exerting its influence upon our boys."

In fact, though they rubbed their eyes, they could scarcely keep them open: they yawned, stretched, turned round, and turned back again.

"Come, come, up, my lads!" exclaimed I once again; "the more we venture to parley with sloth the longer she holds us in her chains. Brave youths like you ought to awake at the first call and leap quick and gaily out of bed."

After this short admonition all came down. Prayers and breakfast over, we returned to the seaside to complete the unloading of the raft, that it might be ready for sea on the ebbing of the tide. I was not long, with the additional assistance I had, in taking two cargoes to Falcon's Stream. At our last trip the tide was nearly up to our craft. I immediately sent back my wife and three children, and remained with Fritz waiting until we were quite afloat, when observing Jack hovering round us and dilatory in following his mother, I perceived his wish, and assented to his embarking with us. Shortly after the tide was high enough for us to row off. Instead of steering for Safety Bay to moor our vessels there securely I was tempted by the fineness of the weather to go out again to the wreck, which it was with considerable difficulty we reached, though aided by a fresh sea-breeze. On our getting alongside it was too late to undertake much, and I was unwilling to cause my wife uneasiness by passing another night on board. I therefore determined to bring away only what could be obtained with ease and speed. In this intention we searched hastily through the ship for any trifling articles that might be readily removed. Jack was up and down everywhere, at a loss what to select. When I saw him again he drew a wheelbarrow after him, shouting and rejoicing at having found such a vehicle for the convenient carriage of our potatoes. But Fritz next disclosed still better news, which was that he had discovered behind the bulk-head amidships a pinnace taken to pieces, with all its appurtenances, and even two small guns for its defence. This intelligence so delighted me that I quitted everything else to run to the bulk-head, when I was convinced of the truth of the lad's assertion. But I instantly perceived that to put it together and launch it into the sea would be a Herculean task, which I relinquished for the present. I then collected some house utensils and whatever else I thought most useful, such as a large copper boiler, some plates of iron, tobacco-graters, two grinding-stones, a small barrel of gunpowder, and another of flints, which I much valued. Jack's barrow was not forgotten. Two more were afterwards found and added. All these articles were hurried into the boat without our stopping to eat or in any manner refresh ourselves, and we re-embarked with speed to avoid meeting the land wind that invariably rose in the evening. As we were safely and happily drawing near to shore, we were struck with the appearance of an assemblage of small figures ranged in a long line on the strand, and that seemed to be viewing us attentively. They were dressed in black, and all uniform, with white waistcoats and full gravats. The arms of these beings hung down carelessly. Now and then, however, they seemed to extend them tenderly, as if they wished to embrace or offer us a token of friendship.

"I really think," said I to the boys, who were steadily gazing at so novel a spectacle, "that we are in the country of the pygmies, and that, having discovered us, they wish to form a friendly alliance."

"But I begin to see," said Fritz, "that the pygmies have beaks, and that their arms are short, dropping wings. What strange birds!"

"You are right, son; they are penguins or ruffs. They are of the stupid species. Ernest killed one soon after our arrival. They are excellent swimmers, but cannot fly; and so confused are they when on land, that they run in the silliest way into danger. Catching such birds as these is a fit sport for none but the indolent."

While we were talking I steered gently towards the shore to enjoy the uncommon sight the longer. But the very moment we got into shallow water, my giddy boy Jack leaped out of his tub up to his waist, and was quickly on land battering with his stick among the penguins before they were aware of his approach, so that half a dozen of them were immediately laid flat. They were not dead, only stunned. The remainder, seeing they were so roughly accosted plunged into the sea, dived, and disappeared.

Fritz murmured audibly at his brother for having frightened them away before he could fire. I could not help laughing at this perpetual shooter of guns, who was so disposed to waste his powder on animals who were to be taken with the hand without resistance. I also taunted Jack a little for having jumped into the water at the risk of being drowned. While I was making these observations the birds that had been merely stunned, gradually recovered, rose upon their legs and began a tottering sort of march with a gravity which irresistibly excited our laughter. I did not allow Jack's game to escape. I took hold of them, tied their legs together with reeds without hurting them, an laid them on the beach while we were landing our treasures. But as the sun declined, and we despaired of finishing before night set in, each of us filled a barrow in order to take home something. I requested that the tobacco-graters and iron plates might be in the first load. To these we added the penguins, living and dead, and then set out. As we drew near Falcon's Stream I heard with pleasure the watchful dogs proclaim our approach with loud barking. They no sooner saw us than they ran up with lively demonstrations of joy, and in the midst of their rough greetings completely overset poor Jack, who was wheeling along his barrow with difficulty and some ill humour, to which he gave vent by two or three lusty cuffs of his fist, which were divided between his friends Turk and Ponto, who so little thought of resenting them that they sprang upon him as often as he took his barrow, and thus renewed the contest, to the no small amusement of his brothers, who ran up to disengage him. My wife was highly pleased with the wheel-barrows, and for the most part with their contents, but she had no partiality for the tobacco graters.

"What is the use of these graters?" she exclaimed. "Are our four sons to become snuff-takers? Luckily for myfears the article is not to be obtained in our island."

"No, dear wife," I replied; "and pray do not be uneasy about them. These graters are not for the gratification of our noses. I am too happy in having myself abandoned the habit of snuff-taking to permit my sons to adopt it. Come, children," said I pointing to the penguins, "look after the newcomers to the poultry-yard."

I then directed them to fasten the birds one by one to a goose or a duck, as a means of taming them and inuring them to the society of their companions. This essay, however, was tedious and inconvenient to our feathered animals, who were but slowly reconciled to their singular companions. My wife now showed me a good store of potatoes which she had got in during our absence, and a quantity of the roots I had taken for manioc.

"Father, we have worked very hard indeed," said little Francis. "What will you say when we have a fine crop of maize, melons, dates, and gourds? Mother has planted all these in the potato holes."

"I must tell you, Master Francis," exclaimed his mother, "that you are a little thoughtless babbler. Why did you tell my secret? You have spoiled all the pleasure I promised myself in surprising your father with my new plantation."

I waked the boys very early, for I had promised to teach them a new trade.

"What is it? What is it?" exclaimed they all at once, springing suddenly out of bed and hurrying on their clothes.

Father: "It is the art of baking, my boys, which at present I am no more acquainted with than yourselves. But we will learn it together, and I am much mistaken if we shall not be able to produce some excellent bread, which will be the greater luxury from our having been altogether deprived of it during our residence in this island. Hand me those iron plates that we brought yesterday from the vessel, and the tobacco-graters also."

Mother: "I really cannot understand what tobacco-graters and iron plates can have to do with making bread. A good oven would afford me much better hopes, and this, unfortunately, we do not possess."

Father: "These very iron plates, the same you looked so disdainfully upon no longer since than yesterday, will serve the purpose of the things you are now wishing to have. I cannot, it is true, promise in this early attempt to produce you light and handsome-looking bread; but I can answer that you shall have some excellent-tasted cakes, though they should be a little flat and heavy. We will immediately make our experiment. Ernest, bring, hither the roots found underground; but first, my dear, I must request you to make me a small bag of a piece of the strongest wrapper linen."

My wife set instantly to work to oblige me; but having no great confidence in my talents for making cakes, she first filled with potatoes the large copper boiler we had brought from the ship, and put it on the fire, that we might not find ourselves without something to eat the time of dinner. In the meanwhile I spread a large piece of coarse linen on the ground, and assembled my young ones round me to begin our undertaking. I gave each of the boys a grater, and showed him at the same time how to rest it on the linen, and then to grate the roots of manioc.

A very short time was now sufficient for producing a considerable quantity of ground manioc. By this time my wife had completed the bag. I had it well filled with what we called our pollard, and she closed it effectually by sewing up the end. I was now to contrive a kind of press. I cut a long, straight, well-formed branch of considerable strength from a neighbouring tree, and stripped it of the bark. I then placed a plank across the table we had fixed between the arched roots of our tree, and which was exactly the right height for my purpose, and on this I laid the bag. I put other planks again upon the bag, and then covered all with the large branch, the thickest extremity of which I inserted under an arch, while to the other, which projected beyond the planks, I suspended all sorts of heavy objects, such as lead, our largest hammers, and bars of iron, which, acting with great force as a press on the bag of manioc, caused the sap it contained to issue in streams, which flowed plentifully on the ground.

"Can one make any use of this sap?" asked my wife.

"Certainly we may," I replied. "The negroes use it as food, after mixing with it a considerable quantity of pepper, and, when they can procure them, some sea-crabs. The Europeans, on the other hand, leave it to settle in vessels till it has formed a sediment. They then pour off the liquid part, wash the sediment with fresh water, and place it to dry in the sun. In this manner they obtain from it an excellent sort of starch, which is used for clearing linen. I must tell you that the potato also contains the same sort of substance, which may be put to the same use."

Mother: "But, pray tell me, are we to prepare the whole of this manioc at once? If so, we have at least a whole day's work, and a great part must be spoiled at last."

Father: "Not so, my dear. When the pollard is perfectly dry it may be placed in casks, and being shut closely down, it will keep for years; but you will see that the whole of this large heap will be so reduced in quantity by the operation we are going to apply of baking, that there will be no cause for your apprehension."

Fritz: "Father, it no longer runs a single drop. May we not now set about making the dough?"

Father: "I have no objections: but it would be more prudent to make only a small cake at first by way of experiment, which we will give to the monkey and the fowls, and wait to see the effect, instead of exhausting our whole store at once."

We now opened the bag, and took out a small quantity of the pollard, which already was sufficiently dry. We stirred the rest about with a stick, and then replaced it under the press. The next thing was to fix one of our iron plates, which was of a round form and rather convex, so as to rest upon two blocks of stone at a distance from each other.

Under this we lighted a large fire, and when the iron plate was completely heated we placed a portion of the dough upon it with a wooden spade. As soon as the cake began to be brown underneath it was turned, that the other side might be baked also.

Ernest: "Oh, how nicely it smells! What a pity that we may not eat some of it immediately!"

Jack: "And why not? I would eat some without the least fear; and would not you, Francis?"

As soon as the cake was cold we broke some of it into crumbs, and grave it to two of the fowls, and a larger piece to the monkey, who nibbled it with a perfect relish, making all the time a thousand grimaces to testify his content, while the boys stood by envying the preference he enjoyed.

"But what, I pray you, may there be in that boiling vessel yonder?" said I, turning to my wife.

"It is the penguin that Jack killed and brought home, and now we shall see how it tastes," she replied.

To say the truth, we did not take a fancy to the dish, the bird being of a strong and fishy flavour. Jack, however, was of a different opinion, and he was left at full liberty te regale himself to his appetite's content.

The first thing we did after dinner was to visit our fowls. Those among them which had eaten the manioc were in excellent condition, and no less so the monkey, who gave us sufficient proofs of life and health in the multitude of gambols and grimaces he exhibited.

"Now then, to the bakehouse, young ones!" said I. "To the bakehouse, as fast as you can scamper!"

The grated manioc was soon emptied out of the bag, a large fire was quickly lighted, and when sufficiently hot I placed the boys where a flat surface had been prepared for them, and gave to each a plate of iron and the quantity of a cocoa-nut shellful for them to make a cake apiece, and they were to try who could succeed the best. They were ranged in a half-circle round the place where I stood myself, that they might the better be enabled to observe how I proceeded, and adopt the same method for themselves. The result was not discouraging for a first experiment, though it must be confessed we were now and then so unlucky as to burn a cake. But there was not a greater number of these than served to feed the pigeons and the fowls, which hovered round us to claim their share of the treat. My little rogues could not resist the pleasure of frequently tasting their cake, a little bit at a time as they went on. At length the undertaking was complete. The cakes were put in a dish, and served in company with a handsome share of milk to each person. With this addition, they furnished as an excellent repast. What remained we distributed among our animals and fowls. I observed with pleasure that the penguins which I had preserved alive accommodated themselves perfectly to this kind of food, and that generally they began to lose their former timid behaviour. I therefore indulged my inclination to compassionate their captive state, and ventured to disengage them from their comrades. This indulgence procured me the pleasure of seeing them seemingly in a state of newly-acquired content.

The rest of the day was employed by the boys in making several turns with their wheel-barrows and by myself in different arrangements in which the ass and our sledge had a principal share, both being employed in drawing to Tent House the remaining articles we had brought from the ship. When all this was done we retired to rest, having first made another meal on our cakes, and concluded all with pious thanks to God for the blessings His goodness thought fit to bestow upon us.

## CHAPTER X

From the time of discovering the pinnace, my desire of returning to the vessel grew every moment more and more irresistible. One thing I saw was absolutely necessary, which was to collect all my hands and go provided with sufficient strength to enable me to get her out from the situation where we had found her the day before. I therefore thought of taking with me the three boys. I even wished that my wife should accompany us; but she had been seized with such a horror of the perfidious element as she called it, the sea, that she assured me the very attempt would make her ill, and thus occasion her to be an additional trouble rather than of use. I had some difficulty to prevail upon her to let so many as three of the children go. She made me promise to return the same evening and on no account to pass another night on board the wreck. And to this I was, though with regret, obliged to consent.

After breakfast, then, we prepared for setting out. The boys were gay and on the alert, in the expectation of the pleasure that awaited them, particularly Ernest, who had not yet made a single voyage with us to the vessel. We took with us an ample provision of boiled potatoes and cassave, and, in addition, arms and weapons of every kind. We embarked and reached Safety Bay without the occurrence of any remarkable event. Here we thought it prudent to put on our cork-jackets. We then scattered some food for the geese and ducks which had taken up their abode there, and soon after stepped gaily into our tub-boat, at the same time fastening the new raft by a rope to her stern, so that she could be drawn along. We put out for the current, though not without considerable fear of finding that the wreck had entirely disappeared. We soon, however, perceived that she still remained firm between the rocks. Having got on board, our first care was to load our craft with different stores, that we might not return without some acquisition of comfort for our establishment. Then all on the wings of curiosity and ardour we repaired to that part of the vessel called the bulk-head, which contained the enviable prize, the pinnace. On further observation, it appeared to me that the plan we had formed was subject to at least two alarming and perhaps insurmountable difficulties. The one was the situation of the pinnace in the ship, and the other was the size and weight it would necessarily acquire when put together. The enclosure in which she lay in pieces was far back in the interior of the ship, and close upon the side which was in the water, immediately under the officers' cabin. Several inner timbers of prodigious bulk and weight separated this enclosure from the breach at which only we had been able to get on board, and in this part of the deck there was not sufficient space for us to work at putting the pinnace together, or to give her room should we succeed in completing our business. The breach also was too narrow and too irregular to admit of her being launched from this place, as we had done with our tub-raft. In short, the separate pieces of the pinnace were too heavy for the possibility of our removing them even with the assistance of our united strength. What, therefore, was to be done? And how could we meet so formidable a difficulty? I stood on the spot absorbed in deep reflection, while the boys were running from place to place, conveying everything portable they could find on board the raft.

The cabinet which contained the pinnace was lighted by several small fissures in the timbers, which, after standing in the place a few minutes to accustom the eye, enabled one to see sufficiently to distinguish objects. I discovered with pleasure that all the pieces of which she was composed were so accurately arranged and numbered, that without too much presumption I might flatter myself with the hope of being able effectually, to collect and put them together, if I could be allowed the necessary time and could procure a convenient place. I therefore, in spite of every disadvantage, decided on the undertaking, and we immediately set about it. We proceeded, it must be confessed, at first so slowly as to produce discouragement, if the desire of possessing so admirable a little vessel, quite new, perfectly safe, easy to conduct, and which might at some future day be the means of our deliverance, had not at every moment inspired us with new strength and ardour.

Evening, however, was fast approaching, and we had made but small progress. We were obliged to think of our promise to my wife, and, though with reluctance, we left our occupation and re-embarked. On reaching Safety Bay we had the satisfaction of finding there our kind steward and little Francis. They had been during the day employed in some necessary arrangements for our living at Tent House as long as we should have occasion to continue the excursions to the vessel. This she did to shorten the length of the voyage and that we might be always in sight of each other. This new proof of her kind attention affected me in a lively manner, and I could not sufficiently express the gratitude which I felt, particularly as I knew the dislike she had conceived to living in this spot. I presented her with the valuable cargo we brought, which I knew would give her pleasure, and regretted that I had no better recompense to offer for the voluntary sacrifice she had made to my accommodation. I made the best display I could of two casks of salted butter, three of flour, some small bags of millet-seed and of rice, and a multitude of other articles of utility and comfort for our establishment. My wife rewarded me by the expression of her perfect satisfaction, and the whole was removed to our store-house at the rocks.

We passed an entire week in this arduous undertaking of the pinnace. I embarked regularly every morning with my three sons, and returned every evening, and never without some small addition to our stores. We were now so accustomed to this manner of proceeding that my wife bade us goodbye without concern, and we on our parts left Tent

House without anxiety. She even had the courage to go several times, with no companion but her little Francis, to Falcon's Stream, to feed and take care of the poultry, and to bring back potatoes for our use. As night successively returned we had a thousand interesting things to tell each other, and the pleasure of being together was much increased by these short separations. We even enjoyed with a better appetite the excellent supper our kind hostess at all times took care to prepare for us.

At length the pinnace was completed, and in a condition to be launched. The question now was how to manage this remaining difficulty. She was an elegant little vessel, perfect in every part. She had a small neat deck; and her mast and sails were no less exact and perfect than those of a little brig. It was probable she would sail well from the lightness of her construction, and drawing comparatively little water. We had pitched and towed all the seams that she might be water-tight. We had even taken the superfluous pains of further embellishing by mounting her with two small cannons of about a pound weight, and, in imitation of larger vessels, had fastened them to the deck with chains. But in spite of the delight we felt in contemplating a commodious little vessel, formed for usefulness in all of its parts, and the work as it were of our own industry, yet the great difficulty still remained. The said commodious, charming little vessel still stood fast, enclosed within four walls; nor could I conceive of a means of getting her out. To support the idea of so much time and labour bestowed for no end or advantage was absolutely impossible. To effect a passage through the outer side of the vessel by means of our united industry in the use of all the utensils we had secured, seemed to present a prospect of exertions beyond our powers.

I had found on board a strong iron mortar, such as is used in kitchens. I took a thick oak plank, and nailed to a certain part of it some large iron hooks; with a knife I cut a groove along the middle of the plank, thus furnished, upon it, having previously pitched the mortar all round; and lastly, I made the whole fast to the spot with strong chains crossed by means of the hooks in every direction. Thus I accomplished a sort of cracker, from which I expected to effect a happy conclusion. I hung this infernally-contrived machine against the side of the bulk-head next the sea, having taken previous care to choose a spot in which its action could not affect the pinnace. When the whole was arranged I set fire to the match, the end of which projected far enough beyond the plank to allow us sufficient time to escape. I now hurried on board the raft, into which I had previously sent the boys before applying a light to the match. Though they had assisted in forming the cracker, they had no suspicion of the use for which it was intended, believing all the while it concealed some subject of amusement for their next trip to the vessel. I confess I had purposely avoided giving them the true explanation, from the fear of the entire failure of my project, or that the vessel, pinnace, and all that it contained might in consequence be blown up in a moment. I had naturally, therefore, some reluctance to announce myself before the time as the author of so many disasters.

On our arrival at Tent House, I immediately put the raft in a certain order, that she might be in readiness to return speedily to the wreck when the noise produced by the cracker should have informed me that my scheme had taken effect. We set busily to work to empty her, when, during the occupation, our ears were assailed with the noise of an explosion of such violence, that my wife and the boys, who were ignorant of the cause, were so dreadfully alarmed as instantly to abandon their employment.

We rowed out of the bay with more rapidity than on any former occasion. Curiosity gave strength to our arms. When the vessel was in sight, I observed with pleasure that no change had taken place in the part of her which faced Tent House, and that no sign of smoke appeared. We advanced, therefore, in excellent spirits. But, instead of rowing, as usual straight to the breach, we proceeded round to the side on the inside of which we had placed the cracker. The scene of devastation we had caused now broke upon our sight. The greater part of the ship's side was shivered to pieces; innumerable splinters covered the surface of the water. The whole exhibited a scene of destruction, in the midst of which presented itself our elegant pinnace entirely free from injury! I could not refrain from the liveliest exclamations of joy, which excited the surprise of the boys, who had felt the disposition such a spectacle naturally inspired, of being dejected at the sight of so melancholy an event. They fixed their eyes upon me with the utmost astonishment. "Now then, she is ours!" cried I — "the elegant little pinnace is ours! for nothing is now more easy than to launch her. Come, boys, jump upon her deck, and let us see how quickly we can get her down upon the water."

I now attentively examined the breach we had thus effected, and next the pinnace. I perceived that it would be easy, with the help of the crowbar and the lever, to lower her into the water. In putting her together, I had used the precaution of placing the keel on rollers, that we might not experience the same difficulty as we had formerly done in launching our tub-raft. Before letting her go, however, I fastened the end of a long thick rope to her head, and the other end to the most solid part of the wreck, for fear of her being carried out too far. We put our whole ingenuity and strength to this undertaking, and soon enjoyed the pleasure of seeing our pretty pinnace descend gracefully into the sea, the rope keeping her sufficiently near, and enabling us to draw her close to the spot where I was loading the tub-boat, and where for that purpose I had lodged a pulley on a projecting beam, from which I was enabled also to advance with the fixing of the masts and sails for our new barge. I endeavoured to recollect minutely all the information I had ever possessed on the art of equipping a vessel, and our pinnace was shortly in a condition to set sail.

Two whole days more were spent in completely equipping and loading the beautiful little barge we had now secured. When she was ready for sailing, I found it impossible to resist the earnest importunity of the boys, who, as a recompense for the industry and discretion they had employed, claimed my permission to salute their mother, on approach to Tent House, with two discharges of cannon. These accordingly were loaded, and the two youngest placed themselves, with lighted match in hand, close to the touch-holes, to be in readiness. Fritz stood at the mast to manage the ropes, while I took my station at the rudder. These matters being adjusted, we put off with sensation of lively joy, which was demonstrated by loud huzzas and suitable gesticulation.

Our old friend the tub-raft had been deeply loaded and fastened to the pinnace, and it now followed as an accompanying boat to a superior vessel. We took down our large sail as soon as we found ourselves at the entrance of the Bay of Safety, to have the greater command in directing the barge; and soon the smaller ones were lowered one by one, that we might the more securely avoid being thrown with violence upon the rocks so prevalent along the coast.

Thus, proceeding at a slower rate, we had greater facilities for managing the important affair of the discharge of the cannon. Arrived within a certain distance — "Fire!" cried commander Fritz. The rocks behind Tent House returned the sound. "Fire!" said Fritz again. Ernest and Jack obeyed, and the echoes again majestically replied. Fritz at the same moment had discharged his two pistols, and all joined instantly in three loud huzzas.

"Welcome, welcome, dear ones!" was the answer from an anxious mother, almost breathless with astonishment and joy.

My wife was particularly gratified by these our late adventures. She applauded our skill and perseverance. "But do not," said she, "imagine that I bestow so much commendation without the hope of some return in kind. On the contrary, it is now my turn to claim from you, for myself and little Francis, the same sort of agreeable recompense. For we have not, I assure you, remained idle while the rest were so actively employed for the common benefit. No, not so, little Francis and his mother found means to be doing something also, though not at this moment prepared to furnish such unquestionable proofs as you, by your salutations of cannon and pistol. But wait a little, and our proofs shall hereafter be apparent in some dishes of excellent vegetables which we shall be able to regale you with. It depends, to say the truth, only on yourselves to go with me and see what we have done."

We did not hesitate to comply, and jumped briskly out of the pinnace for the purpose. Taking little Francis by the hand, she led the way, and we followed in the gayest mood imaginable. She conducted us up an ascent of one of the rocks, and stopping at the spot where the cascade is formed from Jackal's River, she displayed to our astonished eyes a commodious kitchen-garden, laid out properly in beds and walks, and, as she told us, everywhere sowed with the seed of useful plants.

"This," said she, "is the pretty exploit we have been engaged in, if you will kindly think so of it. In this spot the earth is so light, being principally composed of decayed leaves, that Francis and I had no difficulty in working it, and then dividing it into different beds — one for potatoes, one for manioc, and other smaller shares for lettuces of various kinds, not forgetting to leave a due proportion to receive some plants of the sugar-cane. You, dear husband, and Fritz will easily find means to conduct sufficient water hither from the cascade, by means of pipes of bamboo, to keep the whole in health and vigour, and we shall have a double source of pleasure from the general prosperity, for both the eyes and the palate will be gratified. But you have not yet seen all. There, on the slope of the rock, I have transplanted some plants of the ananas. Between these I have sowed some melon-seeds, which cannot fail to succeed, thus securely sheltered and in so warm a soil. Here is a plot allotted to peas and beans, and this other for all sorts of cabbage. Round each bed or plot I have sowed seeds of maize, to serve as a border, while on account of its tall and bushy form it will at the same time protect my young plants from the scorching heat of the sun."

I stood transported in the midst of so perfect an exhibition of such kind zeal and persevering industry. I would only exclaim that I should never have believed in the possibility of such a result in so short a time, and particularly with so much privacy as to leave me wholly unsuspicious of the existence of such a project.

It was then decided, after a light but pleasing repast, to return again to our Tree House near Falcon's Stream.

## CHAPTER XI

My first thought the next morning was to fetch the sledge from the wood. I had a double motive for leaving it there, which I had refrained from explaining to my wife to avoid giving her uneasiness. I had formed a wish to penetrate a little further into the soil, and ascertain whether anything useful would present itself beyond the wall of rocks. I was, besides, desirous to be better acquainted with the extent, the form, and general production of our island. I wished Fritz only to accompany me. We took Turk with us. We set out very early in the morning, and drove the ass before us for the purpose of drawing home the sledge.

On reaching the wood of evergreen oaks, we found the sow feeding upon the acorns under the trees. We wished her a good appetite, and begged her to admit us to the honour of partaking her breakfast. As we were quietly picking up some of the acorns, we observed some birds, which occupied the wood in every direction, flying towards us. Some of them were clothed with a plumage of exquisite beauty, and for this once I could not refuse Fritz the pleasure of firing upon them, that we might in consequence obtain a nearer view, and inform ourselves respecting their species. He brought down three. I recognised one to be the great blue Virginia jay, and the other two were parrots. One of the two was a superb red parrot, the other was green and yellow.

We soon arrived at the guava-trees, and a little after at the spot where we had left the sledge in the wood of gourds, when we found our treasures in the best possible condition. As the morning was not far advanced, we entered upon our intended project of penetrating beyond the wall of rocks.

We pursued our way in a straight line at the foot of these massy and solid productions of nature, every moment expecting to reach their extremity, or to find some turn, or breach, or passage through them, that should conduct us into the interior of the island, if, as I presumed, it was not terminated by these rocks. We walked on, continually looking about, that nothing might escape us worthy of notice, or to be enabled to anticipate and avoid such dangers as should threaten. Turk as usual took the lead, the ass followed with lazy steps, shaking his long ears, and Fritz and I brought up the rear. We met from time to time with some small streams, which afforded a most agreeable refreshment. We passed a wood of guava-trees, and fields of potatoes and manioc, the stalks of which perplexed our way; but we were recompensed for this inconvenience by the fine views which everywhere presented themselves, and which the low stature of the plants enabled us to see in perfection. To the right, on the high grounds, we saw hares and agoutis in considerable numbers, amusing themselves on the grass in the morning sun.

We next entered a pretty little grove, the trees of which were unknown to us. Their branches were loaded with large quantities of berries of an extraordinary quality, being entirely covered with a wax which stuck to our fingers as we attempted to gather them.

"Let us stop here", said I to Fritz, "for we cannot do better than collect a great quantity of these berries as a useful present to your mother."

A short time after another kind of object presented itself with equal claims to our attention. It was the singular behaviour of a kind of bird scarcely larger than a chaffinch, and clothed in feathers of a common brown colour. These birds appeared to exist as a republic, there being among them one common nest, inhabited at pleasure by all their tribes. In the sides, which were unequally formed, we observed a quantity of small apertures, seemingly intended as doors and windows to each particular cell of this general receptacle. From a few of these apertures issued some small branches, which served the birds as points of rest for entering and returning. The external appearance of the whole excited the image of an immensely large, open sponge. The birds which inhabited it were very numerous. They passed in and out continually, and I estimated that it might contain at least a million. The males were somewhat larger than the females, and there was a trifling difference in their plumage. The number of the males was very small in proportion to the females.

While we were attentively examining this interesting little colony, we perceived a very small kind of parrot, not much larger than the birds themselves, hovering about the nest. Their gilded green wings and the variety of their colours produced a beautiful effect. They seemed to be perpetually disputing with the colonists, and not unfrequently endeavoured to prevent their entrance into the building. They attacked them fiercely, and even endeavoured to peck at us if we but advanced our hand to the structure. Fritz, who was well trained in the art of climbing trees, was earnestly desirous to take a nearer view of such extraordinary beings, and to secure, if possible, a few individuals. He threw his whole bundle to the ground, and climbed till he reached the nest. He then tried to introduce his hand into one of the apertures, and to seize whatever living creature it should touch in that particular cell. What he most desired was to find a female brooding hen, and to carry both her and the eggs away. Several of the cells were empty, but by perseverance he found one in the situation he wished. But he did not pursue his plan without meeting with the full punishment of his curiosity. He received so violent a stroke from the beak of an invisible bird, that his only care was now to withdraw his hand, which he shook in the air to ease the pain, uttering all the time the most dismal lamentations. But though punished he was not cured of his fault. No sooner had the pain subsided than he ventured a second time to pass his hand into the nest, and succeeded in seizing his prey, which he laid hold of by the middle of the body, and in spite of the bird's resistance, its cries and wailings, he drew it through the aperture and squeezed it into his breast pocket, and buttoning his coat securely, he slid down the tree and reached the ground in safety. The signals of distress sent forth by the prisoner collected a multitude of birds from their cells, who all surrounded him, uttering the most piteous cries and flying at him with their beaks, till he had made good his retreat. The birds pursued him till he was quite close to my side, when, by making a loud noise and waving my pocket-handkerchief, I succeeded in driving them away. Fritz now released the prisoner, and we discovered him to be a beautiful little green parrott, which Fritz entreated he might be allowed to preserve and make a present of to his brothers, who would make a cage to keep him in, and would then tame him and teach him to speak. I did not oppose his request, but thinking we had spent too much time upon this singular bird-colony, I bade him prepare quickly for returning home.

We had proceeded a considerable way, and had reached a wood, the trees of which were unknown to us, though they in a small way resembled the wild fig-tree. The leaves of these tress, at the extremity of the branches, are very thick. In substance tough, like leather, their upper and under surfaces presented different tints. But what surprised us the most was a kind of gum, or bituminous matter, which appeared by some accidental means to issue in a liquid state from the trunk of the tree, and so become immediately hardened by the air. This discovery awakened Fritz's while attention. In Europe he had often made use of the gum produced by cherry trees, either as a cement or varnish, in the process of some of his youthful occupations, and the thought struck him that he could do the same with what he now saw. He accordingly collected with his knife a certain quantity.

As he continued walking he looked frequently at his gum, which he tried to soften with his breath or with the heat of his hand, as he had been accustomed to do with that from the cherry-trees, but he found he could not succeed. On the other hand, his endeavours revealed a still more singular property in the substance that of stretching considerably on being pulled by the two hands at its extremities, and, on letting go, of reducing itself instantly by the power of an elastic principle. He was struck with surprise at this phenomenon, and sprang towards me, repeating the experiment before my eyes, and exclaiming, "Look, Father! If this is not the very kind of Indian rubber we formerly used to rub out the bad strokes in our drawings. See! I can stretch it, and it instantly shrinks back when I let go!"

"Ah! what do you tell me?" cried I with joy. "Such a discovery would be an invaluable benefit.

The best thanks of all will be due to you if you have discovered the true caoutchouc-tree which yields the Indian rubber. Quick, hand it here that I may examine it."

Fritz: "Look, Father, how it will stretch! But I do not, however, understand how it can be so immensely valuable to us."

Father: "Caoutchouc is a kind of milky sap which runs from certain trees, and no doubt from these before us. This liquid is received by those who collect it in vessels placed expressly for the purpose. It is afterwards made to take the form of dark-coloured bottles of different sizes, such as we have seen them, in the following manner. Before the liquid which runs out has time to coagulate, some small earthen bottles are dipped into it a sufficient number of times to form the thickness required. These vessels are then hung over smoke, which completely dries them. The concluding part of the operation is to break the bottle which has served for a mould, and to get out the pieces by the passage of the neck, when the ingredient remains in the complete form of a bottle, soft to the touch, firm in substance, yet flexible and convenient to carry about, from being not liable to break, and may be even used as a vessel to contain liquid if necessary."

Fritz: "The fabrication seems simple enough, so let us try to make some bottles of it, which will be convenient for carrying something for us to drink when we go a long way in pursuit of game."

Father: "Its quality is admirable, too, Fritz, for being made into shoes and boots without seams, if we can add the assistance of earthen moulds of the size of the leg or foot. Now then, I suppose you can understand my reason for the joy expressed at the sight of so unexpected a benefit. We must consider of some means of restoring masses of the caoutchouc to its liquid form, for spreading upon the moulds, and if we should not succeed, we must endeavour to draw it in sufficient quantities, when wanted for use and in its liquid state, from the trees themselves. There is, besides, another use for which this substance is both fit and excellent. It renders waterproof any kind of linen or woollen production to which it may be applied."

Well satisfied with the discovery we had made, we continued our way, endeavouring still farther to explore the wood, which stretched before us to a considerable distance. We were determined to reach the furthest outlet of this great wood of cocoa-trees to examine the dimensions and limits of our empire. In a short time we had taken some observations that enabled us to ascertain this point, and, looking attentively, we recognised the great bay on the right, and on the left Cape Disappointment, which latter had been the farthest point of our earliest excursion.

We began to consider how much farther we would go. The thick bushes of bamboo, through which it was impossible to pass, seemed to furnish a natural conclusion to our journey. We were therefore unable to ascertain whether we should or should not have found a passage beyond the wall of rocks. We perceived, then, no better resource than to turn to the left towards Cape Disappointment, where the luxurious plantations of sugar-canes we had discovered on our first visit now again drew our attention. That we might not return empty-handed to Falcon's

Stream, we each took the pains to cut a large bundle of canes, which we threw across the ass's back, not forgetting the ceremony of reserving one apiece, to refresh ourselves with along the road.

We arrived at Falcon's Stream without any further adventure, and rather early in the evening. Each of the boys seized a sugar-cane and began to suck it, as did their mother also. Nothing could be more amusing than to hear Fritz relate with unaffected interest the recent discoveries we had made.

But when we took out of his pocket the little parrot all alive, there was no bounds to their ecstasy. They jumped about like mad things, and I was obliged to interpose my authority to prevent them tearing him to pieces, in the struggle who should have him first. At length the bird was fastened by the leg to one of the roots of the trees till a cage could be made for him, and was fed with some acorns, which he appeared to relish exceedingly. My wife was delighted with the prospect of the candles I assured her I was now able to furnish. Fritz took a bit of the rubber from his pocket and drew it to its full length, and then let it suddenly go, to the great amusement of little Francis.

Soon after nightfall, being much fatigued, and after partaking of a hearty supper, we all mounted the ladder, and, having carefully drawn it up, we fell, exhausted, into sound and peaceful slumbers.

On the following day, neither my wife nor the boys left me a moment's tranquillity till I had put my manufactory of candles in some forwardness. I therefore set myself to recollect all I had read on the subject.

I put as many berries into a vessel as it would contain, and set it on a moderate fire. My wife in the meantime employed herself in making some wicks with the threads of sail-cloth. When we saw an oily matter of a pleasing smell and light-green colour rise to the top of the liquid the berries had yielded we carefully skimmed it off and out it into a separate vessel, taking care to keep it warm. We continued this process till the berries were exhausted, and had produced a considerable quantity of wax. We next dipped the wicks one by one into it while it remained liquid, and then hung them on the bushes to harden. In a short time we dipped them again, and continued repeating the operation till the candles were increased to the proper size. They were then put in a place and kept till sufficiently hardened for use. We were all eager to judge of our success that very evening by burning one of the candles, and we had reason to be well satisfied. In consequence of this new treasure we should now be able to sit up later, and consequently spend less of our time in sleep. But independently of this advantage, the mere sight of a candle, which for so long a time we had been deprived of, caused ecstasies of joy to all.

Our success in this last enterprise encouraged us to think of another, the idea of which had long been cherished — it was the construction of a cart for the better conveyance of our effects from place to place, instead of the sledge, which caused us so much fatigue to draw.

While I was thus laboriously engaged, the boys and their mother were no less busy in matters of use of convenience, and I now and then left my cart to assist them with my advice; though, to do them justice, I must say that they seldom stood in need of it. They undertook to transplant the greatest part of the European fruit-trees, to place them where they would be in a better situation for growth, according to the properties of each. They planted vine-shoots round the roots of the magnificent tree we inhabited, and round the trunks of some other kinds of trees which grew near. We watched them in the fond anticipation that they would in time ascend to a height capable of being formed into a sort of trellis, and help to cool us by their shade. In the climate we inhabited, the vine requires the protection of the larger trees against the scorching rays of the sun. Lastly, we planted two parallel lines of saplings, consisting of chestnut, cherry, and the common nut trees, to form an avenue from Family Bridge to Falcon's Stream which would hereafter afford us a cool shade in our walks to Tent House.

Our next concern was to introduce, if possible, some shade and other improvements on the barren site of Tent House, and to render our occasional abode or visits there more secure. We began by planting all those sorts of trees that thrive best in the sun, such as lemon, pistachio, almond, mulberry, and lime trees; lastly, some of a kind of orange tree which attains a prodigious size, and bears a fruit as large as the head of a child, and weighs not less than twelve or fourteen pounds. The commoner sorts of nut-trees we placed along the shore in the most favourable situations. The better to conceal and fortify our tent, which enclosed all our stores, we formed on the accessible side of hedge of wild orange and lemon trees, which produce an abundant prickly foliage.

Our continued labours wore out our clothes so fast that another trip to the vessel was absolutely necessary. We had nearly exhausted the stock we had already brought away, and were now absolutely in rags. We feared we saw the time when we should be compelled to renounce the European modes of dress. I had also another reason for wishing to visit the ship. The cart I had just completed disclosed a defect which it was scarcely possible to endure. It was a violent creaking of the wheels at every turn, and in addition the wheels moved so imperfectly round the axle-tree, that the united strength of the ass and the cow could scarcely drag the machine along. It was in vain that, in spite of my wife's reproofs, I applied a little butter now and then; in an hour or two the butter dried, and wheels remained the same.

The first fine day I assembled my three eldest sons, and put my design into execution. We reached the wreck without any striking adventure, and found her still fixed between the rocks, but somewhat more shattered than when we had last seen her. We did not lose a moment in searching for the tubs of pitch, which, with the help of the pulley, we soon conveyed into the pinnace; we next secured the chests of clothes, and whatever remained of ammunition stores — powder, shot, and even such pieces of cannon as we could remove, while those that were too heavy we stripped of their wheels, which might be extremely useful.

But to effect our purpose it was necessary to spend several days in visits to the vessel, returning constantly in the evening, enriched with everything of a portable nature which the wreck contained; doors, windows, locks, bolts, nothing escaped our grasp, so that the ship was now entirely emptied, with the exception of the heavy cannon and three or four immense copper caldrons, which were too heavy to be got into the boat. We by degrees contrived to tie these heavy articles to two or three empty casks well pitched, which would effectually sustain themselves and the cannon above water. When these measures were taken, I came to the resolution of blowing up the wreck. I directed my views to that part of the vessel which had been entirely stripped of everything; I supposed that the wind and tide would convey the beams and timbers ashore, and thus with little pains we should be possessed of a sufficient quantity of materials for erecting a building at some future time.

We accordingly prepared a cask of gunpowder, which we left on board for the purpose. We rolled it to the place most favourable for our views. We made a small opening in its side, and at the moment of quitting the vessel we inserted a piece of matchwood, which we lighted at the last moment, as before. We then sailed with all possible expedition for Safety Bay, where we arrived in a short time. We could not, however, withdraw our thoughts from the wreck and from the expected explosion for a single moment. I had cut the match a sufficient length for us to hope that she would not go to pieces before dark. I proposed to my wife to have our supper carried to a little point of land from whence we had a view of her, and here we waited for the moment of her destruction with lively patience.

About the time of nightfall, a majestic rolling sound like thunder, accompanied by a column of fire and smoke, announced that the ship, so closely concerned with our peculiar destiny, which had brought us to our present abode in a desert, and furnished us there with such vast supplies for general comfort, was that instant annihilated, and withdrawn for ever from the face of man! At this moment, love for the country that gave us birth, that most powerful sentiment of the human heart, sunk with a new force into ours. The ship had disappeared for ever! Could we, then, form a hope ever to behold that country more?

A night's repose in some measure relieved the melancholy of the preceding evening, and I went rather early in the morning with the boys to make further observations as to the effects of this remarkable event. We perceived in the water and along the shore abundant vestiges of the departed wreck, and among the rest, at a certain distance, the empty casks, caldrons, and cannon, all tied together, and floating in a large mass upon the water. We jumped instantly into the pinnace, with the tub-boat fastened to it, and made a way towards them through the numberless pieces of timber &c., that intervened, and in a little time reached the object of our search, which from its great weight moved slowly upon the waves. Fritz with his accustomed readiness tied a rope round two four-pounders, and contrived to fasten them to our barge after which he secured also an enormous quantity of poles, laths, and other useful articles. With this rich booty we returned to land.

We performed three more trips for the purpose

of bringing away more cannon, caldrons, fragments of masts, &c., all of which we deposited for present convenience in Safety Bay. And now began our most fatiguing operation, the removing of such numerous and heavy stores from the boats to Tent House.

My wife, in taking a survey of these our labours, made the agreeable discovery that two of our ducks and one of the geese had been brooding under a large bush, and at the time were conducting their little families to the water. The news produced general rejoicings. Fritz and Ernest looked forward to some luxurious Sunday dinners, and Jack and Francis wondered what the young birds could think when they first saw any human creatures! We in a short time found means to tame them by throwing them occasionally some crumbs of manioc. This last employment, together with the gambols of the little creatures, so forcibly carried our thoughts to Falcon's Stream, that we all conceived the ardent desire of returning to the society of the numerous old friends we had left there. One sighed for his monkey, another for his flamingo; Francis for his parrot, and his mother for her poultry-yard, her various housewifery accommodations and her comfortable bed. We therefore, fixed the next day for our departure, and set about the necessary preparations.

## CHAPTER XII

On entering our new plantation of fruit-trees forming the avenue to Falcon's Stream, we observed that they had not a vigorous appearance, and that they inclined to droop. We therefore immediately resolved to support them with sticks, and I proposed a walk to the vicinity of Cape Disappointment for the purpose of cutting some bamboos. I had no sooner pronounced the words than the three eldest boys and their mother exclaimed at once that they would accompany me. Their curiosity had been excited by the accounts Fritz and I had given of the variety of things we had met with in our visit there. Each found a sound and special reason why he must not fail to be of the party. Our provision of candles was nearly exhausted, and a new stock of berries must therefore be procured, for my wife now repaired our clothes by candle-light, while I employed myself in composing a journal of the events of every day; then, the sow had again deserted us, and nothing could be so probable as that we should find her in the acorn wood; Jack would fain gather some guavas for himself, and Francis must needs see the sugar-canes he sucked with so keen a relish. In short, all would visit this land of Canaan.

We accordingly fixed the following morning, and set out in full procession. For myself, I had a great desire to explore with more attention this part of our island, and to reap some more substantial advantages from its produce. I therefore made some preparations for sleeping, should we find the day too short for all we might have to accomplish. I took the cart instead of the sledge, having fixed some planks across it for Francis and his mother to sit upon when they should be tired. I was careful to be provided with the different implements we might want: some rope machinery I had contrived for rendering the climbing of trees more easy, since we could not always expect to meet with a crab who would obligingly give us his assistance; and lastly, some provisions, consisting of a piece of the salted tortoise, some water in a gourd-flask, and one bottle of wine from the captain's store. When all was placed in the cart, I for this occasion harnessed to it both the ass and the cow, as I expected the load would be increased on our return. We set out, taking the road of the potato and manioc plantations. Our first halt was at the tree of the colony of birds. Close upon the same spot were also the trees whose berries produced the wax for candles, and intermixed with these some of the guava kind. On this second occasion of seeing the birds, I recollected to what species they belonged, which by naturalists is named Loxia gregaria (Sociable Grossbeck).

It was not without much difficulty that we conducted the cart through the thick entangled bushes, the most intricate of which I everywhere cut down, and we helped to push it along with all our strength. We succeeded tolerably well at last, and that the poor animals might have time to rest, we determined to pass several hours in this place which furnished such a variety of agreeable and useful objects. We began by gathering a bagful of the guavas, and after regaling ourselves plentifully upon them, we put the remainder into the cart. We next examined anew, and with close attention, the interesting structure of the nest inhabited by the colony of birds, and concluded, contrary to the opinion I had formerly entertained, that the little green parrot was an invader who had seized upon an empty place, and fixed himself in it, for numerous flocks of the brown-coloured birds now passed in and out, rested upon the bushes which produced the wax, and devoured large quantities of the berries, which explained the reason of their building their singularly-contrived abode in this particular spot. We claimed the same privilege as the birds, and had soon filled another bag with the berries we found means to beat down from the bushes. Seeing them so greedily consumed by those little animals, the boys desired to follow their example, and accordingly tasted them, but found them too insipid for their palate.

We continued our way, and soon arrived at the caoutchouc or gum-elastic trees. I thought we could not do better than to make a halt here, and endeavour to collect a sufficient quantity of the sap to make the different kinds of utensils, and the impenetrable boots and shoes, as I had before proposed. It was with this design that I had taken care to bring with me several of the most capacious of the gourd rinds. I made deep incisions in the trunks, and fixed some large leaves of trees, partly doubled together lengthways, to the place, to serve as a sort of channel to conduct the sap to the vessels I had kept in readiness to receive it. We had not long begun this process before we perceived the sap begin to run out as white as milk, and in large drops, so that we were not without hopes by the time of our return to find the vessels full, and thus to have obtained a sufficient quantity of the ingredient for a first experiment.

We left the sap running, and pursued our way, which led us to the wood of cocoa-trees. From thence we passed to the left, and stopped half-way between the bamboos and the sugar-canes, intending to furnish ourselves with a provision of each. We aimed our course so judiciously, that on clearing the skirts of the wood we found ourselves in an open plain, with the sugar-cane plantations on our left, and on our right those of bamboo interspersed with various kind of palm-trees, and in front the magnificent bay formed by Cape Disappointment, which stretched far out into the sea.

Our next proceeding wasto divide amongst us the different occupations which were the objects of our walk. Some scampered away to the right to cut bamboos, others to the left to secure the sugar-canes, of both of which a large bundle was collected, tied together, and put into the cart. The bodily exertions made by the boys again excited their desire to eat. They sucked some of the canes, but their hunger was not appeased. Their mother, however, refused to let them have the remainder of the provisions, and they therefore cast a longing eye to the tops of the trees, where they saw a great number of cocoa-nuts suspended. After a short deliberation it was determined that two of them should venture on climbing to the top, a height of from sixty to eighty feet, and with the hatchet, which would be fastened to their waist, should beat them down. Fritz and Jack had no hesitation. They selected the trees which had most fruit for their attempt, and proceeded a considerable way. But the trunks were too thick to be easily grasped by their legs and arms, and having no place of rest for either, they were obliged to come down again much quicker than they had ascended. It was now my part to suggest something.

"I have something here," said I, "which may help. Here are some pieces of prepared shagreen, which must be tied round your legs. Then with this cord I shall fasten you by the body to the trunk of the tree, but so loosely that it will move up and down when you do. By sitting occasionally on this cord, you will be enabled to rest when necessary, and so push on by little and little. This manner of climbing trees is practised by savages with success. At first you will make but slow progress, but after two or three experiments you will find no further difficulty."

The boys had listened with entire attention. Excited by the description I had made, they eagerly demanded to be equipped for the experiment, and their success exceeded our expectation. They with tolerable ease reached the top of the tree, where the thick-tufted foliage furnished a commodious seat, and from whence they sent forth exulting salutations. They now took their hatchets and set to work, when presently a shower of cocoa-nuts descended, from which the persons below had barely time to escape by running to a distance. The monkey, having observed what was going on, took the fancy of imitating his young masters, and sprang from the ground into one of the trees, he with his teeth and his paws, sent down as many nuts as the hatchet. He then came down with equal swiftness, and seating himself on the ground began to crack one of the nuts, making all the time such strange grimaces as to occasion us all much merriment. The two boys had descended with more caution than the monkey, and with perfect safety. They received our compliments on the skill and address they had evinced in so promptly making themselves masters of so valuable an art.

It was now past noon. As we had determined to pass the night in this enchanting spot, we began to think of forming some large branches of trees into a sort of hut, as is practised by the hunters in America, to shelter us from the dew and the coolness of the air, for we had dismissed our fears of the approach of wild beasts, not having in so long a time been visited by any. I accordingly set to work. I had brought a piece of sail-cloth with me from Falcon's Stream, and I drove some stakes into the ground, and covered them with it, filling the opening in the front with some branches I had cut for the purpose. While we were engaged in our work, which was nearly completed, we were suddenly roused by the loud braying of the ass, which we had left to graze at a distance but a short time before. As we approached nearer to the place, we saw him throwing his head in the air and kicking and prancing about in a more extraordinary manner; and while we were thinking what could be the matter, he set off on a full gallop, leaving us in a state of astonishment at all we saw.

Fatigued, and vexed with the loss of the ass, which was so eminently useful to us, I entered the hut, which I found complete and provided with the necessary branches strewed on the ground for sleeping, and with some reeds for making a fire, which the freshness of the evening air rendered agreeable to all. It served us also for cooking our supper. After it had been partaken by us all, we were glad to lie down upon the branches and enjoy the blessing of sleep. When all was safe, I watched and replenished the fire till midnight, rather from habit than the fear of wild beasts, and then took possession of the little corner assigned me near my slumbering companions.

The following morning found us all in good health, and thankful for the Divine protection we had enjoyed. We breakfasted on some milk from the cow, some boiled potatoes, and a small portion of Dutch cheese, and formed during our meal the plan of the business of the day. We had in vain hoped that night and our bright fire would have brought back the fugitive. We had, therefore, no resource but to depend upon our own exertions for recovering him. It was accordingly decided that one of the boys and myself, attended by the two dogs, should seek him in every direction through the bamboo plantations, and if we should not succeed in finding him, I was to return to the hut, where I knew my wife and the other boys would have been employed in cutting sugar-canes and collecting a provision of the different articles we had met with, preparatory to our return the following day to Falcon's Stream. As I was to take both the dogs, I left the two eldest boys to protect little Francis and his mother, and took for my own escort the agile Jack, who was almost beside himself with joy at this determination.

We took, then, our hatchets, our firearms, a little saw for the cocoa-nuts we might happen to find, and began our course with the first dawn of the morning. We soon reached the bamboo plantation, which we entered, preceded by the dogs, and found means, though not without difficulty, to force ourselves along its intricate entanglements. After the most exhausting fatigue, and when we were on the point of relinquishing all further hope, we discovered the print of the ass's hoofs, on the soil, which inspired us with new ardour in the pursuit. After spending a whole hour in further endeavours, we at length, on reaching the skirts of the plantation, perceived the sea in the distance, and soon after found ourselves in an open space which bounded the great bay. A considerable river flowed into the bay at this place, and we perceived that the ridge of rocks which we had invariably observed to the right extended to the shore, terminating in a perpendicular precipice, leaving only a narrow passage between the rocks and the river, which during every flux of the tide must necessarily be under water, but which at that moment was dry and passable. The probability that the ass would prefer passing by this narrow way to the hazard of the water, determined us to follow in the same path. Wa had also some curiosity to ascertain what might be found on the other side of the rocks, for as yet we were ignorant whether they formed a boundary to our island or divided it into two portions; whether we should see there land or water. We continued to advance, and at length reached a stream which issued foaming from a large mass of rock and fell in a cascade into the river. The bed of this stream was so deep, and its course so rapid, that we were a long time finding a part where it might be most practicable for us to cross. When we had got to the other side, we found the soil again sandy and mixed with a fertile kind of earth. In this place we no longer saw naked rock, and here we again discovered the print of the ass's hoof.

By observing with attention, we beheld with astonishment that there were the prints of the feet of other animals also, that they were somewhat different from those of the ass, and much larger. Our curiosity was so strongly excited by this appearance that we resolved to follow the tracks. They conducted us to a plain at a great distance, which presented to our wondering eyes the exhilarating image of a terrestrial paradise. We ascended a hill which partly concealed from our view this scene, and then with the assistance of the glass we looked down upon a range of country exhibiting every rural beauty that the mind could conceive, and where a profound tranquillity had seemed to take up its abode.

By straining our eyes, however, as far as we could see, we thought we perceived at a great distance some specks that seemed to be in motion. We hastened towards the spot, and as we drew nearer, to our inexpressible surprise discovered a group of animals. We accordingly drew near by a path we found in a plantation of reeds, that we might not give notice of our approach, being ignorant of the kind of animal we were about to meet. We had not gone far when the soil became so marshy, and the reeds entangled to such a degree, that we were obliged to get out of the plantation and wind along on the outside. We were soon near the animals, which we perceived consisted of rather a numerous troop of wild buffaloes. This animal is formed at first sight to inspire the beholder with terror. It is endowed with an extraordinary degree of strength, and two or three of them were capable of destroying us in a moment, should they feel the desire of attacking us. My alarm was so great that I remained for a few moments fixed to the spot like a statue. By good luck the dogs were far behind us, and the buffaloes, having never beheld the face of man, gave no sign of fear or of displeasure at our approach. They stood perfectly still, with their large round eyes fixed upon us in astonishment. Those which were lying down got up slowly, but not one among them seemed to have any hostile disposition towards us. We drew back quietly, and prepared our firearms. It was not, however, my intention to make use of them in any way but for defence, being sensible that we were not strong enough for the encounter, and recollecting also to have read that the sound of a gun drives the buffalo to a state of desperation. I therefore thought only of retreating, and with Jack, for whom I was more alarmed than for myself, was proceeding in this way, when unfortunately Turk and Ponto ran up to us, and we could see were noticed by the buffaloes. The animals instantly and altogether set up such a roar as to make our nerves tremble with the shock of so terrible a noise. Our brave Turk and Ponto, fearless of danger, ran among the troop in spite of all our efforts to detain them, and, according to their manner of attacking, laid hold of the ears of a young buffalo which happened to be standing a few paces nearer to us than the rest. Although the creature began a tremendous roar and motion with his hoofs, they held him fast, and were dragging him towards us. Thus hostilities had commenced, and unless we could resolve to abandon the cause of our valiant defenders, we were now forced upon the measure of open war, which, considering the strength and number of the enemy, wore a face of the most pressing and inevitable danger. Our every hope seemed now to be in the chance of the terror that the buffaloes would feel at the noise of our musketry, which for the first time would assail their organs, and perhaps excite them to flight.

With, I must confess, a palpitating heart and trembling hands, we fired both at the same moment. The buffaloes, terrified by the sound and by the smoke, remained for an instant motionless, as if struck by a thunderbolt, and then one and all betook themselves to flight with such incredible rapidity that they were soon beyond the reach of our sight. We heard their loud roaring from a considerable distance which by degrees subsided into silence, and we were left with only one of their terrific species near us. This one, a cow, was no doubt the mother of the young buffalo which the dogs had seized and still kept a prisoner. She had drawn near on hearing its cries, and had been wounded by our guns, but not killed. The creature was in a furious state. After a moment's pause she took aim at the dogs, and with her head down was advancing in her rage, and would have gored them to death, if I had not prevented her by firing upon her with my double-barrelled gun, and thus putting an end to her existence.

The young buffalo still remained a prisoner, with his ears in the mouths of the dogs, and the pain occasioned him to be so furious that I was fearful he might do them some injury. I therefore determined to advance and give them what assistance I might find practicable. To say the truth, I scarcely knew in what way to effect this. The buffalo, though young, was strong enough to revenge himself if I were to give the dogs a sign to let go his ears. I had the power of killing him with a pistol at a stroke, but I had a great desire to preserve him alive and to tame him, that he might be a substitute for the ass, which we now had no hope of recovering. I found myself altogether in a perplexing state of indecision, when Jack suddenly and unexpectedly interposed a most effective means for accomplishing my wishes. He had his string with balls in his pocket. He drew it out hastily, and making a few steps backward, he threw it so skilfully as to entangle the buffalo completely, and throw him down. As I could not approach him safely, I tied his legs by two together with a very strong cord. The dogs released his ears, and from this moment we considered the buffalo as our own.

I took my knife from my pocket, and held a piece of string in my hand in readiness. I placed myself before the buffalo, and taking hold of his snout I made a hole in his nostril, into which I quickly inserted the string, which I immediately tied so closely to a tree that the animal was prevented from the least motion of the head, which might have inflamed the wound and increased his pain.

The first attempt I made to pull the cord found him docile and ready to accommodate his motions to our designs, and I perceived that we might now begin our march. I left him for a short time to make some other preparations.

I was unwilling to leave so fine a prey as the dead buffalo behind us. I, therefore, after considering what was to be done, began by cutting out the tongue which I sprinkled with some of the salt we had, in our provision-bag. I next took off the skin from the four feet, taking care not to tear it in the operation. I remembered that the Americans use these skins, which are of a soft and flexible quality, as boots and shoes, and I considered them as precious articles. I lastly cut some of the flesh of the animal with the skin on, and salted it.

We now seated ourselves under the shade of a large tree, and as we ate the remaining portion of our provisions we amused ourselves with an animated review of the scene which had been passing. Our dogs were no less busily employed in greedily devouring the flesh of the buffalo.

As we were not disposed to leave the spot in a hurry, I desired Jack to take the saw and cut down a small quantity of the reeds, which, from their enormous size, might hereafter be of use to us. We set to work, but I observed that he took pains to choose the smallest.

"What shall we do," said I, "with these small-sized reeds? You were thinking, I presume, of providing a bagpipe to announce a triumphal arrival to our companions!"

"You are mistaken, Father," answered Jack; "I am thinking rather of some candlesticks to present to Mother, who will find them useful."

I now helped him to choose some reeds, and soon after we set out on our return home.

We had so many and such heavy articles to remove, that I did not hesitate to dismiss, for that day, all thoughts of looking further for the ass, that we might return the sooner to our companions to relieve any uneasiness they might have felt at our long stay, and also to be myself satisfied respecting their safety during our absence. I began now to think of untying the young buffalo, and on approaching him perceived with pleasure that he was asleep, which afforded me a proof that his wound was not extremely painful. When I awoke him he gave a start as I began to pull him gently with the string. But he afterwards seemed to forget his pain, and followed me without resistance. I fastened another string to his horns, and led him on by drawing both together, and he performed the journey with little inconvenience, and with so unexpected a docility, that to ease ourselves of a part of the heavy burdens we had to carry, we even ventured on the measure of fastening the bundles of reeds upon his back, and upon these we laid the salted pieces of buffalo meat. The creature did not seem aware that he was carrying a load. He followed in our path as before, and thus on the first day of our acquaintance he rendered us an essential service.

In a short time we found ourselves once more at the narrow passage between the torrent and the precipice of the rocks which I have already mentioned. Near this spot we met with a large jackal, who on perceiving us slunk away, but was stoutly pursued by our brave dogs, who overtook him at the entrance of a cavern, and forced him to give them battle.

When we got up to them the jackal was already killed. On examining our prey we found it was a female, and we concluded that she probably had her den and her young ones in the cavern, when, finding all quiet, I gave Jack leave to enter.

For some moments after entering the cavern the complete darkness which prevailed prevented Jack from seeing anything around him, but when his eyes had become accustomed to it, he discerned in a corner a litter of young jackals. The dogs, who accompanied, had before discovered them by the smell. They flew upon the creatures without mercy, and with the exception of one, which Jack found means to preserve, put an end to their existence. He came out of the cavern with the young jackal in his arms, asking if he might have leave to rear it as Fritz had done the monkey. To this I made no objection, as I felt disposed to make an experiment on the effects and power of training on the wild creature, and to observe if it should be possible to succeed in taming him in such a degree as to obtain a good hunting dog.

At all events, it seemed worth while to try. Jack therefore pressed the animal to his bosom and devoured it with kisses, and promised to bestow upon him so faultless an education that he should become the gentlest and most engaging little creature in the world.

We repassed the river in safety, and accompanied by the agreeable noises of its foaming cascades, we regained the hazardous and narrow pass at the turn of the rocks. We, however, proceeded with caution, and finding ourselves safe on the other side, we thought of quickening our pace to arrive the sooner at the hut. We accordingly had the happiness to rejoin our friends before the close of the evening; and though we were somewhat fatigued, yet in other respects we were well and satisfied with the success of our various undertakings. We were received with the liveliest demonstrations of joy, and, as usual, a thousand questions asked at once.

## CHAPTER XIII

We commenced early the next day a business which we had long determined to engage in. It was to plant bamboos close to all the young trees, to support them effectually in their growth. We quitted our tree with great alertness, having our cart loaded with canes and a large pointed iron to dig holes in the ground. We left my wife this time with only her little Francis, requesting them to prepare us a plentiful dinner. In addition to these performances, they volunteered the melting some of the wax berries for our store of candles.

We did not take the buffalo with us, as I wished to give it a day's rest for its nose to heal up, and the cow was sufficient for drawing the load of light bamboo canes. Before setting out we gave the buffalo a few handfuls of salt to ingratiate ourselves with our horned companion. This treat pleased him so highly that he showed by many signs his inclination of accompanying us, to prevent which we were compelled to fasten him securely till we were out of sight.

We began our work at the entrance of the avenue which we had formed, and nearest to Falcon's Stream. The walnut, chestnut and cherry trees we had planted in a regular line and at equal distances we found disposed to bend considerably, seemingly as they had been directed by the wind. I took the task of making holes with the implement upon myself, which, as the soil was light, I easily performed, taking care to go deep enough to fix the stake firmly. In the meantime the boys selected the bamboos, cut them of equal lengths, and pointed the ends to go into the ground. When they were all fixed we threw up the earth compactly about them, and fastened the saplings by the branches to them with some long straight tendrils of a plant which we found near the spot.

Towards noon, a keen appetite hastened our return to Falcon's Stream, where we found an excellent and plentiful dinner prepared by our good and patient steward, of which the palm-tree cabbage was the chief dish. We all agreed that to eat of a better or more delicate food was impossible; and Ernest, who had procured it, received the thanks of all the board.

When the sharpness of hunger was appeased, a new subject was introduced which I and my wife had been seriously revolving for some time. She found it difficult and even dangerous to ascend and descend our tree by the rope-ladder. We never went there but on going to bed, and each time felt an apprehension that one of the children, who scrambled up like cats, might make a false step and perhaps be lamed for ever. Bad weather might come on and compel us for a long time together to seek an asylum in our aerial apartment, and consequently to ascend and descend oftener.

My wife addressed me constantly on the subject, incessantly asking whether I could not invent some easier and less perilous mode of getting to our dwelling. I smiled at her confidence, and I assured her that if I were an enchanter or magician no desire of hers should remain ungratified, and that with a single touch of my wand I would instantly produce for her a commodious firm staircase of perfect workmanship. I had, however, to acknowledge myself at a loss for the means to effect such an accommodation for her. Still, her reiterated appeals and my own anxiety had often made me reflect if the thing were really possible. A staircase on the outside was not to be thought of; the considerable height of the tree rendered that impracticable, as I had nothing to rest it on, and should be at a loss to find beams to sustain it. But I had for some time formed the idea of constructing winding stairs within the immense trunk of the tree, if it should happen to be hollow, or I could contrive to make it so. Francis had excited this idea in speaking of the bees.

"Did you not tell me, dear wife," said I, "that there is a hole in the trunk of this enormous tree of ours, in which a swarm of bees is lodged?"

"Without doubt," answered she. "It was then little Francis was so severely stung in attempting to thrust in a stick. Look at it yourself, you will see the bees go in and come out in throngs."

"Then," replied I, "we have only to examine how far this excavation goes, whether it extends to the roots, and what the circumference of it is. This done, we shall have gained the first difficult step in favour of our staircase."

All my children seized the idea with ardour. They sprang up, and prepared themselves to climb the tops of the roots like squirrels, to succeed in striking at the trunk with axes, and to judge from the sound how far it was hollow. But they soon paid dearly for their attempt. The whole swarm of bees, alarmed at the noise made against their dwelling, issued forth, buzzing with fury, attacked the little disturbers, began to sting them, stuck to their hair and clothes, and soon put them to flight, bearing along with them their enemies, and uttering lamentable cries. My wife and I had some trouble to stop the course of this uproar, and cover the stings with fresh earth to allay the smart. Jack, whose temper was on all occasions rash, had struck exactly upon the bees' nest, and was more severely attacked by them than the rest. It was necessary, so serious was the injury, to cover the whole of his face with linen. The less active Ernest got up the last, and was the first to run off when he saw the consequences, and thus avoided any further injury than a sting or two. But some hours elapsed before the other boys could open their eyes or be in the least relieved from the acute pain that had been inflicted. When they grew a little better, the desire of being avenged of the insects that had so roughly used them had the ascendant in their minds. They teased me to hasten the measures for getting everything in readiness for obtaining possession of their honey. The bees in the meantime were still buzzing furiously round the tree. I prepared tobacco, a pipe, some clay, chisels, hammers, &c. I took the large gourd long intended for a hive, and I fitted a place for it by nailing a piece of board on a branch of the tree. I made a straw roof for the top to screen it from the sun and rain. As all this took up more time than I was aware of, we deferred the attack of the fortress to the following day, and got ready for a sound sleep, which completed the cure of the wounded patients.

Next morning, almost before dawn, all were up and in motion. The bees had returned to their cells, and I stopped the passages with clay, leaving only a sufficient aperture for the tube of my pipe. I then smoked as much as was requisite to stupefy the little warlike creatures. Not having a cap with a mask, such as bee-catchers usually wear, nor even gloves, this precaution was necessary. At first a humming was heard in the hollow of the tree, and a noise like a gathering tempest, which died away by degrees. All was become calm, and I withdrew my tube without the appearance of a single bee. Fritz had got up by me. We then began with a chisel and a small axe to cut out of the tree, under the bees' holes of entrance, a piece three feet square. Before it was entirely separated I repeated the fumigation, lest the stupefaction produced by the first smoking should have ceased, or the noise we had been just making revived the bees. As soon as I supposed them quite lulled again, I separated from the trunk the piece I had cut out, producing as it were the aspect of a window, through which the inside of the tree was laid entirely upon to view, and we were filled at once with joy and astonishment on beholding the immense and wonderful work of this colony of insects. There was such a stock of wax and honey that we feared our vessels would be insufficient to contain it. The whole interior of the tree was lined with honeycombs. I cut them off with care, and put them in the gourds the boys constantly supplied me with. When I had somewhat cleared the cavity, I put the uppercombs, in which the bees had assembled in clusters and swarms, into the gourd which was to serve as a hive, and placed it on the plank I had purposely raised. I came down, bringing with me the rest of the honeycombs, with which I filled a small cask, previously well washed in the stream. Some I kept out for a treat at dinner, and had the barrel carefully covered with cloths and planks, that the bees, when attracted by the smell, might be unable to get at it. We then sat round the table, and regaled ourselves plentifully with the delicious and odoriferous treat of the honey. Having finished our meal, my wife put by the remainder, and I proposed to my sons to go back to the tree, in order to prevent the bees from swarming again there on being roused from their stupor, as they would not have failed to do but for the precaution I took of passing a board at the aperture and burning a few handfuls of tobacco on it, the smell and smoke of which drove them back from their old abode whenever they attempted to return to it. At length they desisted from approaching it, and became gradually reconciled to their new residence, where their queen, no doubt, had settled herself.

We soon after these operations proceeded to examine the inside of the tree. I sounded it with a pole from the opening I had made towards the top, and a stone fastened to a string served us to sound the bottom, and thus to ascertain the height and depth of the cavity. To my great surprise, the pole penetrated without resistance to the branches on which our dwelling rested, and the stones descended to its roots. The trunk, it appeared, had wholly lost its pith, and most of its wood internally; nothing, therefore, was more practicable then to fix winding stairs in the capacious hollow, which should reach from top to bottom. I determined to begin our construction that very day.

We began to cut into the side of the tree towards the sea a doorway equal in dimensions to the door of the captain's cabin, which we had removed with all its framework and windows. We next cleared away from the cavity all the rotten wood, and rendered the interior even and smooth, leaving sufficient thickness for cutting out resting places for the winding stairs. I then fixed in the centre the trunk of a tree ten or twelve feet high and a foot thick, completely stripped of its branches, in order to carry my winding staircase round it. On the outside of this trunk, and the inside of the cavity of our own tree, we formed grooves, so calculated as to correspond with the distances at which the boards were to be placed to form the stairs. These were continued till I had got to the height of the trunk round which they turned. The window I had opened at the top to take out the honey gave light enough. I made a second aperture below, and a third above it, and thus completely lighted the whole ascent. I also effected an opening near our room, that I might conveniently finish the upper part of the staircase. A second trunk was fixed upon the first, and firmly sustained with screws and transverse beams. It was surrounded, like the other, with stairs cut slopingly. Thus we happily eventually effected the undertaking of conducting a staircase to the level of our bed-chamber. If my staircase was not in strict conformity to the rules of architecture, it at least answered the purpose it was built for, that of conducting us with safety and shelter to our nocturnal residence. To render it more solid and agreeable I closed the spaces between the steps with boards. I then fastened two strong ropes, the one descending the length of the little tree, the other along the side of the large one, to assist in case of slipping. I fixed the sash-windows taken from the captain's cabin in the apertures we had made to give light to the stairs. When the whole was complete, it was so pretty, solid, hand convenient that we were never tired of going up and coming down it, and I fear I must add, for the sake of truth, with no small admiration of our united talents. I must, however, candidly own that we succeeded in this arduous attempt by mere dint of efforts, patience, industry, and time, for it occupied us for many weeks together with no intermission.

I will briefly narrate the few remarkable occurrences that took place during the construction of our staircase.

A few days after the commencement of our staircase, the two she-goats gave us two kids, and our ewes five lambs, so that we now saw ourselves in possession of a pretty flock. But lest the domestic animals should follow the example of the ass, and run away from us, I tied a bell to the neck of each. We had found a sufficient number of bells in the vessel, which had been shipped for trading with the savages, it being one of the articles they most value. We could now immediately trace a deserter by the sound, and bring it back to the fold.

Next to the winding stairs my chief occupation was the management of the young buffalo, whose wound in the nose was quite healed, so that I could lead it at will with a cord or stick passed through the orifice. I preferred the latter method, which answered the purpose of a bit, and I resolved to break in this spirited beast for riding as well as drawing. It was already used to the shafts, and very tractable in them.

We were scarcely up one morning, and had got to work in putting the last hand to our winding staircase, when we heard at a distance two strange, peculiar kind of voices that resembled the howlings of wild beasts, mixed with hissings and sounds of some creature at its last gasp, which I was at a loss to explain, and I was not without uneasiness. Our dogs, too, pricked up their ears, and seemed to wet their teeth for a sanguinary combat with a dangerous enemy.

We judged it prudent to put ourselves in a state of defence. We loaded our guns and pistols, placed them together within our castle in the tree, and prepared to repel vigorously any hostile attack from that quarter.

At this very instant the howlings were renewed, and quite close to us. Fritz got as near the spot as he could, listened attentively and with eager looks, then threw down his gun and burst into a loud laughter, exclaiming: "Father, it is our ass — the deserter comes back to us, chanting the hymn of return! Listen! do you not hear his melodious braying in all the varieties of the gamut?"

Shortly after, we had the satisfaction of seeing among the trees our old friend Grizzle, moving towards us leisurely, and stopping now and then to browse. But to our great joy we perceived in his train one of the same species of very superior beauty, and when it was nearer I knew it to be a fine onagra or wild ass, which I conceived a strong desire to possess, though at the same time aware of the extreme difficulty there would be in taming and rendering him subject to our use. Without delay I descended the ladder with Fritz, desiring his brothers to keep still. I consulted my privy-councillor on the means of surprising and taking the stranger captive. I got ready, as soon as possible, a long cord with a running knot, one end of which I tied fast to the root of a tree. The noose was kept open with a little stick slightly fixed in the opening so as to fall of itself on the cord being thrown round the neck of the animal, whose efforts to escape would draw the knot closer. I also prepared a piece of bamboo about two feet long, which I split at the bottom, and tied fast at the top to serve as nippers. Fritz attentively examined my contrivance, without seeing the use of it.

I therefore told him my project of catching it by the noose, which I gave him to manage, as being nimbler and more expert than myself. The two asses drew nearer and nearer to us. Fritz, holding in his hand the open noose, moved softly on from behind the tree where we were concealed, and advanced as far as the length of the rope allowed him. The onagra was extremely startled on perceiving a human figure; it sprung some paces backward, then stopped as if to examine the unknown form. As Fritz now remained quite still, the animal resumed its composure and continued to browse. Soon after Fritz approached the old ass, hoping that the confidence that would be shown by it would raise a similar feeling in the stranger. He held out a handful of oats mixed with salt; our ass instantly ran up to take its favourite food, and greedily devoured it; this was quickly perceived by the other. It drew near, raised his head, breathed strongly and came up so close, that Fritz, seizing the opportunity, succeeded in throwing the rope round its neck; the motion and stroke so affrighted the beast that it instantly sprang off, but was checked by the cord, which, in compressing the neck, almost stopped its breath. It could go no farther, and after many exhausting efforts, it sank panting for breath upon the ground. I hastened to loosen the cord and prevent its being strangled. I then quickly threw our ass's halter over its head. I fixed the nose in my split cane, which I secured at the bottom with pack-thread. I wholly removed the noose that seemed to bring the creature into a dangerous situation. I fastened the halter with two long ropes to two roots near us, on the right and left, and let the animal recover itself, noticing its actions, and devising the best way to tame it in the completest manner.

We also guarded against Master Grizzle playing truant again, and tied him fast with a new halter, confining its fore-legs with a rope. I then fastened it and the wild ass side by side, and put before both plenty of good provender to solace their impatience of captivity.

We had now the additional occupation of training the onagra for our service or our pleasure, as might turn out to be most practicable. My boys exulted in the idea of riding it, and we repeatedly congratulated each other on the good fortune which had thus resulted from the flight of our ass. Yet I did not conceal that we should have many difficulties to encounter in taming it, though it seemed to be young and not even to have reached full growth.

At last we ventured to free it by degrees from its restraints, and to ride it as we had done with the buffalo, still keeping the forefeet tied. But notwithstanding this precaution and every preceding means, it proved as fierce and unruly as ever for the moment. The monkey, who was first put on its back, held on pretty well by clinging to its mane, from which it was suspended as often as the onagra furiously reared and plunged. It was therefore for the present impracticable for either of my sons to get upon it. The perverse beast baffled all our efforts, and the perilous task of breaking it was still to be persevered in with terror and apprehension. In the stable it seemed tolerably quiet and gentle, but the moment it was in any degree unshackled, it became wholly ferocious and unmanageable.

I was at length reduced to my last expedient, but not without much regret, as I resolved, if it did not answer, to restore the animal to full liberty. I tried to mount the onagra, and just as in the act of rearing up violently to prevent me, I seized with my teeth one of the long ears of the enraged creature, and bit it till it bled. Instantly it stood almost erect on its hind-feet, motionless, and as stiff as a stake. It soon lowered itself by degrees, while I still held its ear between my teeth. Fritz seized the moment and sprang on its back. Jack, with the help of his mother, did the same, holding by his brother, who on his part clung to the girth. When both assured me they were firmly seated, I let go the ear. The onagra made a few springs less violent than the former, and, checked by the cords on its feet, it gradually submitted, began to trot up and down more quietly, and ultimately grew so tractable that riding it became one of our chief pleasures. My lads were soon expert horsemen, and their horse, though rather long-eared, was very handsome and well broken-in. Thus patience on our part conquered a serious difficulty, and gained for us a proud advantage.

"Wherever," said my wife to me one evening, after one of our first trials, "did you learn this strange notion of biting the animal's ear?"

"I learned it," replied I, "from a horse-breaker whom I fell in with by chance. He had lived long in America, and carried on the skin-trade with the natives, to whom he took in exchange various European goods. He employed in these journeys half-tamed horses of the southern provinces, which are caught with nooses. They are at first unruly and resist burdens, but as soon as the hunter bites one of their ears they become mild and submissive, and they become so docile that anything may be done with them. Till now I thought this singular mode of taming a wild beast fabulous, but the young onagra convinces me of the truth of the accounts I heard."

## CHAPTER XIV

During the training of the wild ass, which we named Lightfoot, a triple brood of our hens had given us a crowd of little feathered beings. Forty of these at least were chirping and hopping about us, to the great satisfaction of my wife, whose zealous care of them sometimes made me smile. Most women's hearts are so imbued with maternal love as to excite in them a fondness for whatever bears a similitude to infancy. Thus my admirable partner, far from complaining of the trouble such a number of young chickens gave her, took delight in it, and was constantly admiring them. Yet her care and admiration did not prevent her appropriating a part of them to the table, and sending the remainder in small colonies to feed and breed in the desert, where we could find them as they were wanted for our use.

"Here," she said, "are animals of real utility in a family, far beyond your monkeys and jackals, that do nothing but eat, and are unfit to be eaten."

This increase of our poultry reminded us of the necessity of an undertaking we had long thought of, and was not in prudence to be deferred any longer. This was the building between the roots of our great tree covered sheds for all our bipeds and quadrupeds. The rainy season, which is the winter of these countries, was drawing near, and to avoid losing most of our stock it was requisite to provide shelter.

We began by forming a kind of roof above the arched roots of our tree, and employed bamboo canes for the purpose. The longest and strongest supported the roofing in the place of columns, the smaller more closely united, and composed the roof itself. I filled up the interstices with moss and clay, and I spread over the whole a thick coat of tar. By these means I formed a compact and solid covering, capable of bearing pressure. I then made a railing round it, which gave the appearance of a pretty balcony, under which, between the roots, were various stalls sheltered from rain and sun, that could easily be shut and separated from each other by means of planks nailed upon the roots. Part of them were calculated to serve as a stable and yard, part as an eating-room, a store-room, &c., and as a hay-loft to keep our hay and provisions dry in.

This work was soon completed. But afterwards it was necessary to fill these places with stores of every kind for our supply throughout the wet season. In this task we engaged diligently, and went daily here and there with our cart to collect everything useful, and that might give us employment whilst the weather confined us to the house.

One evening, on our return from digging up potatoes, as our cart, loaded with bags, drawn by the buffalo, ass and cow, was gently rolling along, seeing still a vacant place in the vehicle, I advised my wife to go home with the two younger boys whilst I went round by the wood of oaks with Ernest and Fritz to gather as many sweet acorns as we could find room for. We had still some empty sacks. Ernest was accompanied by the monkey, who seldom left him, and Fritz was on the onagra, which he had appropriated to himself, inasmuch as he had helped to take and tame it, and indeed because he knew how to manage it better than his brothers. Notwithstanding the onagra was so well broken in for riding, it continued to be very mettlesome and restive in the shafts, to which we could not inure it. Occasionally it submitted to our putting a loaded sack or two on its back, but we could seldom prevail even this without Fritz being seated in front. He would then take them to the house, and thus was rendered of some general use.

When we reached the oaks, Lightfoot was tied to a bush, and we set actively to work to gather the acorns that had dropped from the trees. And now Ernest came forward, driving the monkey before him, and carrying his hat with the utmost care. He had stuck his girdle full of narrow sharp-pointed leaves in shape like a knife-blade, which reminded me of the production named sword-grass; but I did not pay much attention, as I was too busily engaged in our egg-hunt, and considered his decoration as childishness.

"I am going to take them home, they will please Francis," said he. "They are like swords, and will be the very thing he will like for a plaything."

I applauded Ernest's idea, and encouraged him and Fritz to be thus ever considerate for the absent, so as to prove they could never be forgotten. It was now time to think of moving homeward. My two sons filled the bags with acorns and put them on Lightfoot. Fritz could not refrain from trotting on briskly, but he went rather faster than he intended on setting out. He had taken a handful of the pointed leaves with him, which he whisked before the ears and eyes of onagra till the animal was frightened, lost all restraint, and darting forward with him, hurried away bags and rider at such a rate that we soon lost sight of them. Anxious for his safety, we followed as fast as possible, though out of sight of him all the way, but on our arrival at Falcon's Stream we had the satisfaction of finding him there in perfect safety. His mother indeed had been somewhat alarmed in seeing him dash in like a thunderbolt, but firmly seated between the bags on Master Lightfoot, who stopped short with wonderful precision at his stable door.

Francis for a short time was highly amused with his swordleaves, and then, like all children, who are soon tired of their toys, he grew weary of them, and they were thrown aside. Fritz picked up some of them that were quite soft and withered. He held up one which was pliable as a riband in the hand.

"My little fellow", said he to his brother, "you can make whips of your sword-grass. Take up the leaves and keep them for this purpose, they will be of use in driving your goats and sheep." It had been lately decided that it should be the business of Francis to lead these to pasture.

"Well then, help me to make them," said the child.

They sat down together, Francis divided the leaves into long narrow slips, and Fritz ingeniously platted them into whip-cords. As they were working, I saw with pleasure the flexibility and strength of the bands. I examined them more closely, and found they were composed of long fibres. This discovery led me to surmise that this supposed sword-grass might be a very different thing, and not improbably the flax-plant of New Zealand. This was a valuable discovery in our situation. I knew how much my wife wished for the production, and that it was the article she felt most the want of. I therefore hastened to communicate the intelligence to her, upon hearing which she expressed the liveliest joy.

"This," said she, "is the most useful thing you have found. I entreat you lose not a moment in searching for more of these leaves, and bring me the most you can of them. I will make you stockings, shirts, clothes, thread, ropes... In short, give me flax, looms, and frames, and I shall be at no loss in the employment of it."

I could not help smiling at the scope she gave to her imagination on the bare mention of flax, though so much was to be done between the gathering the leaves and having the cloth she was already sewing in idea. Fritz whispered a word in Jack's ear. Both went to the stable and without asking my leave, one mounted Lightfoot, the other the buffalo, and galloped off towards the wood so fast that I had no time to call them back. They were already out of sight. Their eagerness to oblige their mother in this instance pleaded their forgiveness, and I suffered them to go on without following them, purposing to proceed and bring them back if they did not soon return.

In waiting for them I conversed with my wife, who pointed out to me with all the animation and spirit of useful enterprise so natural to her character, the various machinery I must contrive for spinning and waving her flax for the manufactory of cloths, with which she said she should be able to equip us from head to foot, in speaking of which her eyes sparkled with the love of doing good, the purest kind of joy, and I promised her all she desired of me.

In a quarter of an hour our deserters came back on a full trot. Like true hussars they had foraged the woods and heavily laded their cattle with the precious plant, which they threw at their mother's feet with joyful shouts. We could not blame their abrupt departure. Jack made us laugh in recounting with his accustomed vivacity and drollery at what a rate he had trotted his buffalo to keep up with Lightfoot, and how his great horned horse had thrown him by a side leap.

Fritz: "How is flax prepared, Father, and what is meant by steeping it?"

Father: "Steeping flax or hemp is exposing it in the open air, by spreading it on the ground to receive the rain, the wind, and the dew in order in a certain degree to liquefy the plant. By this means the ligneous parts of the flax are separated with more ease from the fibrous; a kind of vegetable glue that binds them is dissolved, and it can then be perfectly cleaned with great facility, and the parts selected which are fit for spinning."

My wife suggested that we should soak the flax in Flamingo Marsh, and begin by making up the leaves in bundles, as they do hemp in Europe. We agreed to her proposal, and joined in this previous and necessary preparation of the flax during the rest of the day.

Next morning the ass was put to the small light car, loaded with bundles of leaves. Francis and the monkey sat on them, and the remainder of the family gaily followed with shovels and pick-axes. We stopped at the marsh, divided our large bundles into smaller ones, which we placed in the water, pressing them down with stones and leaving them in this state till our sovereign should direct us to remove and set them in the sun to dry, and thus render the stems soft and easy to peel.

A fortnight after my wife told us the flax was sufficiently steeped. We then took it out of the water and spread it on the grass in the sun, where it dried so well and rapidly that we were able to load it on our cart the same evening, and carry it to Falcon's Stream, where it was put by till we had time to attend further to it, and make beetles, wheels, reels, carding-combs, &c. as required by our expert and skilful flax-manufacturer. It was thought best to reserve this task for the rainy season, and to get ready what would be then necessary during our confinement within doors. Uninformed as we were as to the duration of this season, it was highly important to lay in a competent stock of provisions for ourselves and for all the animals. Occasional slight showers, the harbingers of winter, had already come on. The temperature, which hitherto had been warm and serene, became gloomy and variable. The sky was often darkened by clouds, the stormy winds were heard, and warned us to avail ourselves of the favourable moment to collect everything that would be wanted.

Our first care was to dig up a full supply of potatoes and yams for bread, with plenty of coco-nuts and some bags of sweet acorns.

It occurred to us while digging, that the ground being thus opened and manured with the leaves of plants, we might sow in it to advantage, the remainder of our European corn. Notwithstanding all the delicacies this stranger land afforded us, the force of habit still caused us to long for the bread we had been fed with from childhood. We had not yet laid ourselves out for regular tillage, and I was inclined to attempt the construction of a plough of some sort as soon as we had sufficient stock of corn for sowing. For this time, therefore, we committed it to the earth with little preparation. The season, however, was proper for sowing and planting, as the ensuing rain would moisten and swell the embryo grain. We accordingly expedited the planting of the various palm-trees we had discovered in our excursions, at Tent House, carefully selecting the smallest and the youngest. In the environs we formed a large handsome plantation of sugar-canes, so as to have hereafter everything useful and agreeable around us, and thus be freed from the usual toil and loss of time in procuring them.

These different occupations kept us several weeks in unremitting activity of mind and body. Our cart was incessantly in motion, conveying home our winter stock. Time was so precious that we could not even make regular meals, and limited ourselves to bread, cheese, and fruits in order to shorten them, to return quickly to our work, and despatch it before the bad season should set in.

Unfortunately the weather changed sooner than we had expected, and than, with all our care, we could be prepared for. Before we had completed our winter establishment, the rain fell in such heavy torrents that little Francis, trembling, asked me whether Father Noah's deluge was coming on again. And I could not myself refrain from painful apprehension in surmising how we should resist such a body of water, that seemed to change the whole face of the country into a perfect lake.

The first thing to be done, and which gave us all sensations of deep concern, was to remove without delay our aerial abode, and to fix our residence at the bottom of the tree, between the roots and under the tarred roof I had erected; for it was no longer possible to remain above, on account of the furious winds that threatened to bear us away, and deluged our beds with rain through the large opening in front, our only protection here being a piece of sail-cloth, which was soon dripping wet and rent to pieces. In this condition we were forced to take down our hammocks, mattresses, and every article that could be injured by the rain. And most fortunate did we deem ourselves in having made the winding stairs which sheltered us during the operation of the removal. The stairs served afterwards for a kind of lumber-room. We kept in it all we could dispense with, and most of our culinary vessels, wich my wife fetched as she happened to want them. Our little sheds between the roots, constructed for the poultry and the cattle, could scarcely contain us all, and the first days we passed in this manner were painfully embarrassing, crowded all together, and hardly able to move in these almost dark recesses, which the foetid smell from the close-adjoining animals rendered almost insupportable. In addition, we were half stifled with smoke whenever we kindled a fire, and drenched with rain when we opened the doors. For the first time since our disaster we sighed for the comfortable houses of our dear country. But what was to be done? We were not there, and to lose courage and our temper would only increase the evil. I strove to raise the spirits of my companions and obviate some of the inconveniences. The now doubly-precious winding stair was, as I have said, every way useful to us. The upper part of it was filled with numerous articles that gave us room below. As it was lighted and sheltered by windows, my wife often worked there, seated on a stair, with her little Francis at her feet. We confined our live stock to a smaller number, and gave them a freer current of air, dismissing from the stalls those animals that would be at no loss in providing for themselves. That we might not lose them altogether, we tied bells round their necks. Fritz and I sought and drove them in every evening that they did not spontaneously return. We generally got wet to the skin and chilled with cold during the employment, which induced my wife to contrive for us a kind of clothing more suitable to the occasion. She took two seamen's shirts from the chest we had recovered from the wreck, and, with some pieces of old coats, she made us a kind of cloth hoods joined together at the back, and well formed for covering the head entirely. We melted some elastic gum, which we spread over the shirts and hoods. The articles thus prepared answered every purpose of waterproof overalls that were of essential use and comfort to us. Our young rogues were ready with their derision the first time that they saw us in them, but afterwards they would have been rejoiced to have had the same. This, however, the reduced state of our gum did not allow of, and we contented ourselves with wearing them in turn, when compelled to work in the rain, from the bad effects of which they effectually preserved us.

As to the smoke, our only remedy was to open the door when we made a fire. And we did without as much as we could, living on milk and cheese, and never making a fire but to bake our cakes. We then availed ourselves of the opportunity to boil a quantity of potatoes and salt meat enough to last us a number of days. Our dry wood was also nearly expended, and we thanked Heaven the weather was not very cold, for had this been the case our other trials would have been much increased. A more serious concern was our not having provided sufficient hay and leaves for our European cattle, which we necessarily kept housed to avoid losing them. The cow, the ass, the sheep, and the goats, the two last of which were increased in number, required a large quantity of provender, so that we were ere long forced to give them our potatoes and sweet acorns; which, by the by, they found very palatable, and we remarked that they imparted a delicate flavour to their milk. The cow and the goats amply supplied us with that precious article. Milking, cleaning the animals, and preparing their food occupied us most of the morning, after which we were usually employed in making flour of the manioc root, with which we filled the large gourds, which were previously placed in rows. The gloom of the atmosphere and our low windowless habitation sensibly abridged our daylight. Fortunately we had laid in a huge store of candles, and felt no want of that article. When darkness obliged us to light up, we got round the table, when a large taper fixed on a gourd gave us an excellent light, which enabled my wife to pursue her occupation with the needle; while I, on my part, was writing a journal, and recording what the reader has perused of the narrative of our shipwreck and residence in this island, assisted from time to time by my sons and my wife, who did not cease to remind me of various incidents belonging to the story. To Ernest who wrote a fine hand, was entrusted the care of writing off my pages in a clear legible character. Our kind and faithful steward often surprised us agreeably on our return from looking after the cattle, by lighting up a faggot of dried bamboo, and quickly roasting by the clear and fervent heat it produced a chicken, pigeon, duck or penguin from our poultry yard, or some of the thrushes we had preserved in butter, which were excellent, and welcomed as a treat to reward extraordinary toil. Every four or five days, she made us new fresh butter in the gourd churn. This, with some deliciously fragrant honey spread on our manioc cakes, formed a collation that would have raised the envy of European epicures.

The fragments of our meals belonged in right to our domestic animals, as part of the family. We had the two dogs, the young jackal, and the monkey to feed. They relied with just confidence on the kindness of their respective masters, who certainly would have deprived themselves to supply the wants of their helpless dependants. If the buffalo, the onagra, the pig had not found sustenance abroad, they must have been killed or starved, and that would have given us much pain. In the course of these discomforts it was unanimously resolved on that we would not pass another rainy season exposed to the same evils. Even my beloved consort, who felt such a predilection for the abode at Falcon's Stream, was frequently a little ruffled and out of temper with our inconvenient situation, and insisted more than any of us on the propriety of building elsewhere a more spacious and winter residence. She wished, however, to return to our castle in the tree every summer, and we all joined with her in that desire. The choice of a fresh abode now engrossed our attention, and Fritz in the midst of consultation came forward triumphantly with a book he had found in the bottom of our clothes-chest. "Here," said he, "is our best counsellor and model, Robinson Crusoe. Since Heaven has destined us to a similar fate," said he, "whom better can we consult? As far as I remember, he cut himself an habitation out of the solid rock. Let us see how he proceeded. We will do the same, and with greater ease, for he was alone. We are six in number, and four of us able to work."

"Well spoken, son", said I. "This activity and courage gives me pleasure; let us then strive to be as ingenious as Robinson Crusoe."

"And why not?" observed Jack. "Have we not an island, rocks, and tools from abroad as good as he had, and, as brother Fritz says, more hands to use them?"

We assembled, and read the famous history with an ardent interest. It seemed, though so familiar, quite new to us. We entered earnestly into every detail and derived considerable information from it, and never failed to feel lively gratitude towards God, who had rescued us all together, and not permitted one only of us to be cast a solitary being on the island.

Francis repeated his wish to have a Man Friday; Fritz thought it better to be without such a companion, and to have no savages, warfare and encounters. The final result of our deliberations was to go and survey the rocks round Tent House, and to examine whether any of them could be excavated for our purpose.

Our last job for the winter, undertaken at my wife's solicitation, was a beetle for her flax and some carding-combs. I filed large nails till they were even, round and pointed. I fixed them at equal distances in a sheet of tin, and raised the sides of it like a box. I then poured melted lead between the nails and the sides, to give firmness to their points, which came out four inches. I nailed this tin to a board, and the contrivance was fit for work. My wife was impatient to use it, and the drying, peeling, and spinning her flax became from this time a source of inexhaustible delight.

## CHAPTER XV

I can hardly describe our joy when, after many tedious and gloomy weeks of rain, the sky began to brighten, the sun to dart its benign rays on the humid earth, the winds to be lulled, and the state of the air became mild and serene. We issued from our dreary hovels with joyful shouts, and walked round our habitation breathing the enlivening balmy air, while our eyes were regaled with the verdure beginning to shoot forth on every side. Reviving nature opened her arms, every creature seemed reanimated, and we felt the genial influence of that glorious luminary which had been so long concealed from our sight, now returning like a friend who has been absent, to bring us back blessings and delight. We rapidly forgot in new sensations the embarrassments and weary hours of the wet season, and with jocund, hopeful hearts looked forward to the toils of summer as enviable amusements.

The vegetation of our plantation of trees was rapidly advancing. The seed we had thrown into the ground was sprouting in slender blades that waved luxuriantly, a pleasing tender foliage adorned the trees, the earth was enamelled with an infinite variety of flowers, whose agreeable tints diversified the verdure of the meadows. Odorous exhalations were diffused through the atmosphere. The song of birds was heard around; they were seen between the leaves joyfully fluttering from branch to branch; their various forms and brilliant plumage heightened this delightful picture of the most beautiful spring, and we were at once struck with wonder and penetrated with gratitude towards the Creator of so many beauties.

Our summer occupations commenced by arranging and thoroughly cleaning Falcon's Nest, the order and neatness of which the rain and dead leaves blown by the wind had disturbed. In other respects, however, it was not injured, and in a few days we rendered it completely fit for our reception. The stairs were cleared, the rooms between the roots reoccupied, and we were left with leisure to proceed to other employments. My wife lost not a moment in resuming the process of her flax industry. Our sons hastened to lead the cattle to the fresh pastures, already dried by the sun; whilst it was my task to carry the bundles of flax into the open air, where, by heaping stones together, I contrived an oven sufficiently commodious to dry it well. The same evening we all set to work to peel, and afterwards to beat it and strip off the bark, and lastly to comb it with my carding machine, which fully answered the purpose. I took this somewhat laborious task on myself, and drew out such distaffsful of long soft flax ready for spinning, that my enraptured wife ran to embrace me, to express her heartfelt acknowledgement, requesting me to make her wheel without delay, that she might enter upon her favourite work.

At an earlier period of my life, I had practised turnery for my amusement; now, however, I was unfortunately destitute of the requisite utensils. But as I had not forgotten the arrangement and component parts of a spinning-wheel and reel, I by repeated endeavours found means to accomplish those two machines to my wife's satisfaction, and she fell so eagerly to spinning as to allow herself no leisure even for a walk, and scarcely time to dress our dinners. Nothing so much delighted her as to be left with her little boy, whom she employed to reel as fast as she could spin, and sometimes the other three were also engaged in turns at the wheel to forward her business while she was occupied in culinary offices. Not one of them was found so tractable as the cool-tempered, quiet Ernest, who preferred this to more laborious exertions, though such was our want of linen and clothes that we ought all readily and even eagerly to have joined in procuring them. But our excursions and the necessary liberty they involved were more agreeable to us than this female occupation. Our first visit was to Tent House, as we were anxious to ascertain the ravages of winter there, and we found them much more considerable than at Falcon's Stream. The tempest and rain had beaten down the tent, carried away a part of the sail-cloth, and made such havoc amongst our provisions, that by far the largest portion of them was spotted with mildew, and the remainder could be only saved by drying them instantly. Luckily, our handsome pinnace had been spared. It was still at anchor, ready to serve us in case of need; but our tub-boat was in too shattered a state to be of any further service.

In looking over the stores we were grieved to find the gunpowder most damaged, of which I had left three barrels in the tent instead of placing them in a more sheltered situation in the cavity of the rock. The contents of two were rendered wholly useless. I thought myself fortunate on finding the remaining one in tolerable condition, and derived from this great and irreparable loss a cogent motive to fix upon winter quarters where our stores and wealth would not be exposed to such cruel dilapidations.

Notwithstanding the gigantic plan suggested by the enterprising characters of Fritz and Jack, I had little hope of being able to effect the excavation of a dwelling in the side of the rock. Robinson Crusoe found a spacious cavern that merely required enlarging and arrangement; no such cavity was apparent in our rock, which bore the aspect of primitive existence, and was of extreme hardness, so that with our limited powers it seemed that three or four summers would scarcely have sufficed to execute the design. Still, the earnest desire of a more substantial habitation to defend us from the elements perplexed me incessantly and I resolved to make at least the attempt of cutting out a recess that should contain the gunpowder, the most valuable of all our treasures. With this resolution I set off one day, accompanied by my two valiant workmen, Fritz and Jack, leaving their mother at her spinning with her assistants, Ernest and Francis. We took with us pickaxes, chisels, hammers, and iron levers, to try what impression we could make on the rock. I chose a part nearly perpendicular, and much better situated than our tent. The view from it was enchanting, for it embraced the whole range of Safety Bay, the banks of Jackal River and Family Bridge, and many of the picturesque projections of the rocks. I marked out with charcoal the circumference of the opening we wished to make, and we began the heavy toil of piercing the quarry. We made so little progress the first day, that in spite of all our courage we were tempted to relinquish our undertaking. We persevered, however, and my hope was somewhat revived as I perceived the stone was of a softer texture as we penetrated deeper. We concluded from this, that the ardent rays of the sun striking upon the rock had hardened the external layer, and that the stone within would increase in softness as we advanced. This proved to be the case, and when I had cut about a foot in depth we could loosen the rock with the spade like dried mud. This determined me to proceed with double ardour, and my boys assisted me in the task with a zeal beyond their years.

After a few days of assiduous labour we measured the opening, and found we had already advanced seven feet into the rock. Fritz removed the fragments in a barrow, and discharged them in a line before the place to form a sort of terrace. I applied my own labour to the upper part to enlarge the aperture; Jack, the smallest of the three, was able to get in and cut away below. Jack worked a long iron bar sharpened at the end. When he was driving this in with a hammer, to loosen a particularly large piece of rock, he suddenly bawled out:

"It is pierced through, Father! Fritz, I have pierced it through!"

"Ha, ha! Master Jack at his jokes again! But let us hear; what have you pierced? Is it the mountain? Not your hand or foot, is it, Jack?" cried I.

Jack: "No, no, it is the mountain!" (the rocks resounding with his usual shout of joy). "Huzza, huzza! I have pierced the mountain!"

Fritz now ran to him.

"Come, let us see," cried he. "It is no doubt the globe at least you have pierced. You should have pushed on your tool boldly till you reached Europe, which they say is under our feet. I should have been glad to peep into that hole."

Jack: "Well then, peep you may, I can assure you; but I hardly know what you will see. Now, come and look how far the iron is gone in, and tell me if it is all my boasting. If there were not a hollow space behind, how could it penetrate the rock so easily?"

"Come here, Father," said Fritz. "This is really extraordinary. His iron bar seems to have got to a hollow place. See, it can be moved in every direction."

I approached, thinking the incident worth attention. I took hold of the bar, which was still in the rock, and pressing it forcibly from one side to another, I made a sufficient aperture for one of my sons to pass. I observed that in reality the rubbish fell within the cavity, the extent of which I could not ascertain, but I judged from the falling of the stones that it was not much deeper than the part we stood on. My two lads offered to go in together to examine it. This, however, I firmly opposed. I even made them remove themselves from the opening, as I smelled the bad air that issued abundantly from it, and began myself to feel giddiness in consequence of having gone too near; indeed I was compelled to withdraw quickly, and inhale a purer air.

"Beware, my dear children," said I in terror, "of entering such a perilous cavern. Life might be suddenly extinguished there."

Jack: "What, lose our lives, Father! Do you think, then, it contains lions or tigers? Only give me a gun, and let me speak a word to them."

Fritz: "How can you think such animals could live there? Father may indeed fear that it is inhabited by serpents or vipers."

Jack: "And what should hinder us pray from killing serpents or vipers?"

"I admire," said I, "your courage, my brave Jack, but it shall not be tried on this occasion. Neither lions, serpents, nor men are there, yet the danger still exists. How would my young hero acquit himself when, on entering the aperture, he should feel his respiration totally cease?"

Jack: "Not be able to breathe! And why not?"

Fritz: "Because the air is foul, and therefore unfit for breathing, and those who are exposed to it must of course be suffocated. But in what manner, Father, is the air foul?"

Father: "I fear it is full with noxious vapours that would suffocate."

Jack: "Then all to be done is to be off quickly when one feels a stoppage of breath."

Father: "This is certainly the natural course, when it can be taken; but the suffocation in such air usually begins by a dizziness of the head, so violent as to intercept motion, which is followed by an insurmountable oppression; efforts are made to breathe, fainting follows, and without speedy help a sudden death takes place. But there is an infallible test of bad air of the kind I believe this to be; fire does not burn in it. We must try to light a fire in this hole."

The boys now hastened to gather some dry moss, which they made into bundles. They then struck a light, and set fire to them, and then threw the moss blazing into the opening; but, as I had described, the fire extinguished at the very entrance, thus proving that the air within was very bad. We then made a very large fire near the opening, which we hoped would set up a draught, and gradually draw out the bad and admit good air. We were the more confident of this taking place, as we already observed a current of air outwards at the bottom of our hole. We kept the fire burning for some hours. Then we again threw in some lighted straw into the cavern, and found, to our great satisfaction, the bundles thrown in were entirely consumed. We could accordingly reasonably hope nothing was to be feared from the air. There still remained the danger of plunging into some abyss, or of meeting with a body of water. From these considerations I thought it more prudent to defer our entrance into this unknown recess till we had lights to guide us through it. I despatched Jack on the buffalo to Falcon's Stream, to impart our discovery to his mother and two brothers, directing him to return with them, and bring all the tapers that were left. My intention was to fasten them together on a stick to form a large torch, and thus illuminated proceed with our whole troop to examine the interior of this grotto. I had not sent Jack on his embassy without a meaning; the boy possessed from nature a lively and poetical imagination. I knew he would tell his mother such wonders of the grotto, that in spite of the charms of her spinning-wheel he would induce her to accompany him without delay, and bring us lights to penetrate the obscure sanctuary.

Overjoyed at his commission, Jack sprang on the buffalo, which he had nearly appropriated to himself, gaily smacked his whip, and set off so boldly that I almost trembled for his safety. The rash intrepid boy was unencumbered by fear, and made a complete race horse of his horned steed.

In waiting his return I proposed to Fritz to widen the entrance of the subterraneous grotto, to remove the rubbish, and make a way for his mother to pass in easily. After labouring three or four hours we saw them coming up in our car of state — the one I had equipped for the potatoes, and which was now drawn by the cow and the ass, and conducted by Ernest. Francis, too, played his part in the cavalcade, and contended with his brother for the ropes that served as reins. Jack, mounted on his buffalo, came prancing before them, blew through his closed hand in imitation of a French horn, and now and then whipped the ass and cow to quicken their motion. When they had crossed Family Bridge, he came forward on the gallop, and when he got up to us, jumped off the beast, shook himself, took a spring or two from the ground, and thus refreshed ran up to the car to hand his mother out like a true and gallant knight.

I immediately lighted the torches, but instead of tying them together, as I had intended, I preferred that each should take one in his right hand, an implement in his left in case of accident, a taper in his pocket, and flint and steel. Thus we entered the rock in solemn procession. I took the lead, my sons followed me, and their beloved mother, with the youngest, brought up the rear, her interest and curiosity not unalloyed with tender apprehensions. Indeed I myself felt that sort of fear which an unknown object is apt to excite; even our dogs that accompanied us betrayed some timidity, and did not run before as usual. We had scarcely advanced four paces within the grotto when all was changed to more than admiration and surprise. The most beautiful and magnificent spectacle presented itself. The sides of the cavern sparkled like diamonds, the light from our six tapers was reflected from all parts, and had the effect of a grand illumination. Innumerable crystals of every length and shape hung from the top of the vault, which, uniting with those of the sides, formed pillars, altars, entablatures, and a variety of other figures, constituting the most splendid masses. We might have fancied ourselves in the palace of a fairy, or in an illumined temple. In some places all the colours of a prism were emitted from the angles of the crystals, and gave them the appearance of the finest precious stones. The waving of the lights, their bright coruscations, dark points here and there occurring, the dazzling lustre of others — the whole, in short, delighted and enchanted the sight and the fancy.

The astonishment of my family was so great as to be almost ludicrous. They were all in a kind of dumb stupor, half-imagining it was a dream. I now formed a particular conjecture as to the nature of the crystallizations, namely, that I was in a grotto of rock-salt. The discovery of this fact, which no longer admitted a doubt, pleased us all exceedingly. The shape of the crystals, their little solidity, and finally their saline taste, were decisive evidences.

How highly advantageous to us and our cattle was this superabundance of salt, pure and ready to be shovelled out for use, and preferable in all respects to what we collected on the shore.

My wife was charmed with our good fortune in having happened to cut into the rock at this very spot. I observed that in all probability the mine extended a long way, and that I should have discovered salt had I opened at any other part, though such a wonderful grotto might not have been found everywhere.

As we advanced in the grotto, remarkable figures formed by the saline matter everywhere presented themselves. Columns reaching from the bottom to the top of the vault appeared to sustain it, and some even had cornices and capitals; here and there undulating masses which at certain distances resembled the sea. From the variegated and whimsical forms we beheld, fancy might make a thousand creations at its pleasure; windows, large open cupboards, benches, church ornaments, grotesque figures of men and animals, some like polished crystals or diamonds, others like blocks of alabaster.

We viewed with unwearied curiosity this repository of wonders, and we had all lighted our second taper, when I observed on the ground in some places a number of crystal fragments that seemed to have fallen off from the upper part. Such a separation might recur at any moment, and therefore I thought it prudent to retire, as other loosened pieces might unexpectedly fall on us. I directed my wife and three of the children to place themselves in the entrance, while Fritz and I carefully examined every part that threatened danger. We loaded our guns with ball and fired them in the centre of the cavern; one or two fell, the rest remained immovable, though we went round with long poles and struck all we could reach. We at length felt confident that there was nothing to fear, and that we might proceed to fit up our new habitation without dread of accident. Our joy on this important discovery did not fully declare itself till after these trials. Loud exclamations, mixed with numerously varied questions, projects, consultations, now succeeded to our mute astonishment. Many schemes were formed for converting this beautiful grotto into a convenient and agreeable mansion for our abode. All the force of our imagination was centred in that point. The greatest difficulty was removed; we had possession of the most eligible premises; the whole business now was to turn them to the best account, and how to effect this was our unceasing theme. Some voted for our immediate establishment there, but they were opposed by more sagacious counsel, and it was resolved that Falcon's Stream should continue to be our headquarters till the end of the year.

## CHAPTER XVI

The lucky Discovery of a previously-existed cavern in the rock had, as must be supposed, considerably lessened our labour. Excavation was no longer requisite; I had more room than was wanted for the construction of our dwelling. To render it habitable was the present object, and to do this did not seem a difficult task. The upper bed of the rock in front of the cavern, through which my little Jack had dug so easily, was of a soft nature, and to be worked with moderate effort. I hoped also that, being now exposed to the air and heat of the sun, it would become by degrees as hard and compact as the first layer that had given me so much trouble. From this consideration I began, while it retained its soft state, to make openings for the door and windows of the front. This I regulated by the measurements of those I had fixed in my winding staircase, which I had removed for the purpose of placing them in our winter tenement. Intending Falcon's Nest in future as a rural retreat for the hottest days of summer, the windows of the staircase became unnecessary. As to the door, I preferred making one of bark similar to that of the tree itself, as it would conceal our abode the better should we at any time experience invasion from savages or any other enemies. The doors and windows were therefore taken to Tent House, and afterwards properly fixed in the rock. I had previously marked out the openings to be cut for the frames, which were received into grooves for greater convenience and solidity. I took care not to break up the stone taken from the apertures, or at least to preserve it in large pieces, and these I cut with the saw and chisel into oblongs an inch and a half in thickness to serve as tiles. I laid them in the sun, and was gratified in seeing they hardened quickly; I then removed them, and my sons placed them in order against the side of the rock till they were wanted for our internal arrangements.

When I could enter the cavern freely through a good doorway, and it was sufficiently lighted by the windows, I erected a partition for the distribution of our apartments and other conveniences. The extent of the place afforded ample room for my design, and even allowed me to leave several spaces in which salt and other articles could be stored. At the request of my children, I was cautious to injure as little as possible the natural embellishments of this new family mansion. But with all my care I could not avoid demolishing them in the division allotted to the stables. Cattle are fond of salt, and would not have failed to eat away these ornaments. However, to gratify and reward my obedient children, I preserved the finest of the pillars and the most beautiful pieces to decorate our saloon. The large ones served us as chairs and tables, and the brilliant pilasters at once enlivened and adorned the apartment, and at night multiplied the reflection of the lights. I laid out the interior in the following manner. A very considerable space was first partitioned off in two divisions; the one on the right was appropriated to our residence, that on the left was to contain the kitchen, stables and workroom. At the end of the second division, where windows could not be placed, the cellar and store-room were to be formed; the whole separated by partition boards, with doors of communication, so as to give us a pleasant and comfortable abode. Favoured so unexpectedly by what nature had already effected of the necessary labour, we were far from repining ungratefully at what remained to be done, and entertained full hope of completing our undertaking, or at least the chief parts, before winter.

The side we designed to lodge in was divided into three chambers; the first, next the door, was the bedroom for my wife and me, the second a dining parlour, and the last a bed-chamber for the boys. As we had only three windows, we put one in each sleeping-room; the third was situated in the kitchen where my wife would often be. A grating for the present fell to the lot of our dining-room, which, when too cold, was to be exchanged for one of the other apartments. I contrived a good fireplace in the kitchen near the window; I pierced the rock a little above, and four planks nailed together and passed through this opening answered the purpose of a chimney. We made the workroom near the kitchen of sufficient dimensions for the performance of undertakings of some magnitude; it served also to keep our cart and sledge in. Lastly, the stables, which were formed into four compartments to separate the different species of animals, occupied all the bottom of the cavern on this side; on the other were the cellar and magazine. It is readily imagined that a plan of this extent was not to be executed as if by enchantment, and that we satisfied ourselves in the first instance with doing what was most urgent, reserving the residue of our arrangements for winter. Yet every day forwarded the business more than we had been aware of. On every excursion we brought something from Falcon's Stream, that found its place in the new house, where we deposited likewise in safety the remaining provisions from the tent.

The long stay we made at Tent House during these employments furnished us an opportunity of perceiving several advantages we had not reckoned upon, and which we did not defer availing ourselves of. Immense turtles were very often seen on the shore, where they deposited their eggs in the sand, and they regaled us with a rich treat. But, extending our wishes, we thought of getting possession of the turtles themselves for live stock, and of feasting on them whenever we pleased. As soon as we saw one on the sands, one of my boys was despatched to cut off its retreat.

Meanwhile, we approached the animal, quietly and quickly, without doing it any injury, turned it on its back, passed a long cord through the shell, and tied the end of it to a stage which we fixed close to the edge of the water. This done, we set the prisoner on his legs again. It hastened into the sea, but could not go beyond the length of the cord. Apparently it was quite happy, finding plenty of food alongshore, and we enjoyed the idea of being able to take it when wanted. I say nothing of sea-lobsters, oysters, and many other small fishes which we could catch in any number. We at length got used to and to like oysters, and occasionally had a treat of them. The large lobsters, whose flesh was tough and coarse, were given to the dogs, who preferred them to potatoes.

At this time I likewise made some improvements in our sledge, to facilitate the carrying of our stores from Falcon's Stream to pass our Sunday there, and once more offer our pious thanks to the Almighty for all the benefits He had bestowed upon His defenceless creatures.

## CHAPTER XVII

The arrangement of our grotto went on, sometimes as a principal, sometimes as an intermediate occupation, according to the greater or less importance of other concerns. Though we advanced thus with but moderate rapidity, the progress was notwithstanding such as to afford the hope of our being securely established within it by the time of the rainy season.

I had made the fortunate discovery of a bed of gypsum in the neighbourhood of our crystal grotto. I foresaw the great advantages I should derive from it, and tried to find a place in the continuation of the rock which I might be able to blow up. I had soon the good fortune to meet with a narrow slip between the projections of the rocks which I could easily, by the means I proposed, convert into a passage that should terminate in our workroom. I found also on the ground a quantity of fragments of gypsum, and moved a great number of them to the kitchen, where we did not fail to bake a few of the pieces at a time when we made a fire for cooking, which, thus calcined, rubbed into a powder when cold. We obtained a considerable quantity of it which I put carefully into casks for use when the time should come for finishing the interior of our dwelling. My notion was to form the walls for separating the apartments of squares of stone, and to unite them together with a cement of gypsum, which would be the means both of sparing our timber and increasing the beauty and solidity of the work.

It is almost incredible the immense quantity of

plaster we had in a short time amassed. The boys were in a constant state of wonder as they looked at the heap, and protested that believed that I stayed up at night to work.

About two months after the discovery of our grotto we received a visit from a great shoal of fish. We observed Safety Bay to be filled with large fish-es, which seemed eager to push to the shore for the purpose of depositing their eggs among the stones in shallow water. Jack was the first to discover this cir-cumstance. He told me he had seen a great number of whales swimming about in Jackal River, and I sup-posed they were come in pursuit of fish, and that he was glad the greedy creatures would be disappointed. I replied that there must be some delusion in which he had seen, as I could not conceive of a regiment of whales arriving in our diminutive rivulet.

It, however, appeared to me worth while to go and convince myself on the spot respecting these newcomers. Jack and I walked to the mouth of Jackal River, and immediately perceived immense quantities of a large fish moving slowly towards the banks, and some of them from four to eight feet in length. By the pointed snout I supposed them to be sturgeons. Jack now strutted and exulted as if he had gained the command of a regiment of soldiers. "What say you now, Father?" said he. "A single fish of this troop would fill a tub!"

"No doubt," answered I; and with great gravity I added, "Pr'ythee, Jack, step into the river, and fling them to me one by one, that I may take them home to salt and dry."

He looked at me for a moment with a sort of va-cant doubt if I could possibly be in earnest, then seizing suddenly a new idea, "Wait a moment, Father," said he, "and I will do so!" and he sprung off like lightning towards the cavern, from whence he soon returned with a bow and arrows, the bladders of some fish we had previously caught, and a ball of string to catch, as he assured me, every one of the fishes. I looked on with interest and curiosity to mark what was next to happen, while the animation of his countenance, the promptitude and gracefulness of his motions, and the firm determination of his manner, afforded me the highest amusement. He tied the bladders round at certain distances with a long piece of string, to the end of which he fastened an arrow and a small iron hook. He placed the large ball of string in a hole in the ground, at a sufficient distance from the water's edge, and then he shot off his arrow, which the next instant stuck in one of the largest fishes. My young sportsman uttered a shout of joy. At the same moment, Fritz joined us, and witnessed this unexpected feat without the least symptom of jealousy. "Well done, brother Jack!" cried he; "but let me too have my turn." Saying this he ran back and fetched the harpoon and the windlass, and returned to us accompanied by Ernest, who also desired to show his prowess in a contest with our newly-discovered mariners. We were well pleased with their opportune arrival, for the fish Jack had pierced struggled so fiercely that all our endeavours to hold the string were insufficient, and we dreaded at every jerk to see it break and the animal make good its escape. By degrees, however, its strength was exhausted, and aided by Fritz and Ernest we succeeded in drawing it to a bank.

This fortunate beginning of a plan for a fishery

inspired us all with hope and emulation. Fritz eagerly seized his harpoon and windlass. I, for my part, like Neptune, wielded a trident. Ernest prepared the large fishing-rod, and Jack his arrow, with the same apparatus as before, not forgetting the bladders, which were so effectual in preventing the fish from sinking when struck. We were now more than ever sensible of our loss in the destruction of the tub-boat, with which we could have pursued the creature in the water, and have been spared much pains and difficulty. But, on the other hand, such numbers of fishes presented themselves at the mouth of the river that we had only to choose among them. Accordingly, we were soon loaded with them to our heart's content.

Our first concern was to clean our fish thoroughly to preserve them fresh and longer. I took care of the bladders, thinking it might be possible to make a gluc from them, which would be useful for many purposes. I advised my wife to boil some of the smaller fish in oil, similar to the manner of preparing tunny fish in the Mediterranean, and while she was engaged in this process I was at work upon the glue. For the first, I washed the berries in several waters, and then pressed them closely in gourd-rinds in which a certain number of holes had been bored. When the water had run off, the berries were taken out in a substance like cheese, which was then conveyed to the hut to be dried and smoked. For the second, we cut the bladders into strips, which we fastened firmly by one end to a stake, and taking hold of the other with a pair of pincers, we turned them round and round till the strip was reduced to a kind of knot, and these were then placed in the sun to harden, this being the simple and only preparation necessary for obtaining glue from the ingredients. When thoroughly dry, a small quantity is put on a slow fire to melt. We succeeded so well, and our glue was of so transparent a quantity, that I could not help feeling the desire to manufacture some pieces large enough for panes to a window-frame.

When these various concerns were complete, we began to negotiate a plan for constructing a small boat as a substitute for the tub raft, to come close into shore. I had a great desire to make it as the savages do, of the rind of a tree; but the difficulty was to fit on one of sufficient bulk for my purpose, for, though many were to be found in our vicinity, yet each was on some account or other of too much value to be spared. We therefore resolved to make a little excursion in pursuit of a tree of capacious dimensions, and in a situation where it was not likely to yield us fruit, to refresh us with its shade, or to adorn the landscape round our dwelling.

In this expedition we as usual aimed at more than one object. Eager as we were for new discoveries, we yet allowed ourselves the time to visit our different plantations and stores at Falcon's Stream. We were also desirous to secure a new supply of the wax berry of gourds, and of elastic gum. Our kitchen-garden at Tent House was in a flourishing condition; nothing could exceed the luxuriance of the vegetation, and almost without the trouble of cultivation we had excellent roots and plants in abundance, which came in succession, and promised a rich supply of peas, beans, lettuçes, &c. Our principal labour was to give them water freely, that they might be fresh and succulent for use. We had, besides, melons and cucumbers in great plenty, which , during the hottest weather, we valued more than all the rest. We reaped a considerable quantity of Turkey wheat from the seed we had sown, and some of the ears were a foot in length. Our sugar-canes were also in the most prosperous condition, and one plantation of pine-apples on the high ground was also in progress to reward our labour with abundance of that delicious fruit.

This state of general prosperity at Tent House gave us the most flattering expectations from our nurs-eries at Falcon's Stream. Full of these hopes, we one day set out all together for our new somewhat ne-glected former abode.

We arrived at Falcon's Stream, where we intended to pass the night. We visited the ground my wife had so plentifully sowed with grain, which had sprung up with an almost incredible rapidity and luxuriance, and was nearly ready for reaping. We cut down what was fairly ripe, bound it together in bundles, and con-veyed it to a place where it would be secure from the attacks of more expert grain consumers than our-selves, of which thousands hovered round the booty. We reaped barley, wheat, rye, oats, peas, millet, lentils — only a small quantity of each, it is true, but sufficient to enable us to sow again plentifully at the proper season. The plant that had yielded the most was maize, a proof that it best loved the soil and climate. The moment we drew near, a dozen, at least, of large bustards sprang up with a loud rustling noise, which awakened the attention of the dogs. They plunged into the thickest parts, and routed numerous flocks of birds of all kinds and sizes, who all took hastily to flight. Among the fugitives were some quails, who escaped by running, and lastly some kangaroos, whose prodigious leaps enabled them to elude the pursuit of the dogs.

We were so overcome by the surprise such an assemblage of living creatures occasioned as to forget such recourses as we had in our guns. We stood, as it were, stupid with amazement during the first moments, and before we came to ourselves the prey was beyond our reach, and for the most part out of sight.

Jack alone thought of how to repair the error, and also the giving us a specimen of the happy effects of the education he had bestowed on the young jackal. He let him loose, and he slipped slyly away after the birds we supposed were quails, and who were using every effort to escape. The jackal, however, soon overtook them, seized one of them by the wing, and brought it to his master. In the same manner he had carried him at least a dozen more by the time we reached the spot.

At the conclusion of this adventure we hastened forward to arrive the soonest possible at Falcon's Stream. I threw a few more bundles of maize into the cart, and without further delay we arrived at our tree, one and all sinking with faintness from hunger, thirst, and fatigue.

Jack had been able to preserve alive only two of the quails. All the others that the jackal had killed were plucked and put on the spit for supper. The rest of the day was employed in picking the grains of the different sorts of corn from the stalks. We put what we wished to keep for sowing into some gourd-shells, and the Turkey wheat was laid carefully aside in sheaves till we should have time to beat and separate it. Fritz observed that we should also want to grind it, and I reminded him of the hand-mill we had secured from our departed ally, the wrecked vessel.

Fritz: "But, Father, the hand-mill is so small, and so subject to be put out of order. Why should we not contrive a watermill as they do in Europe? We have surely rapid streams of water in abundance."

Father: "This is true, but such a mechanism is more difficult than you imagine; the wheel alone, I conceive, would be an undertaking far beyond our strength or our capacity. I am, however, well pleased with the activity and zeal which prompted your idea, and though I dare not bid you trust in a successful result, yet we may consider whether it may be worth while to bestow upon it further attention. We have time before us, for we shall not want a water-mill till our harvests are such as to produce plentiful crops of corn. In the meantime, let us be thinking, boy, of our proposed excursion for tomorrow, for we should set out at latest by sunrise."

We began our preparations accordingly. My wife chose some hens and two fine cocks, with the intention of taking them with us and leaving them at large to produce a colony of their species at a considerable distance from our dwelling-places. I, with the same view, visited our stable, and selected four young pigs, four sheep, two kids, and one male of each species, our numbers having so much increased that we could well afford to spare these individuals for the experiment. If we succeed in thus accustoming them to the natural temperature and productions of our island, we should have eased ourselves of the burden of their support, and should always be able to find them at pleasure.

The next morning, after loading the cart with all things necessary, not forgetting the rope-ladder and the portable tent, we quitted Falcon's Stream. The animals, with their legs tied, were all stationed in the vehicle. We left abundance of food for those that remained behind. The cow, the ass, and the buffalo were harnessed to the cart. Fritz, mounted on his favourite, the onagra, pranced along before us to ascertain the best and smoothest path for the cavalcade.

We took this time a new direction, which was straight forward between the rocks and the shore, that we might make ourselves acquainted with everything contained in the island we seemed destined for ever to inhabit. In effect, the line proceeding from Falcon's Stream to the Great Bay might be said to be the extent of our dominions, for, though Jack and I had discovered the adjacent exquisite country of the buffaloes, yet the passage to it by the end of the rocks was so dangerous, and at so great a distance, that we could not hope to settle ourselves until its soil, as we had done on our side of the rocks. We found, as usual, much difficulty in pushing through the tall tough grass, and alternately through the thick prickly bushes which everywhere obtruded themselves. We were often obliged to turn aside while I cut a passage with my hatchet. But these accidents seldom failed to reward my toil by the discovery of different samll additions to our general comfort; among others, some roots of trees curved by nature to serve both for saddles and yokes for our beasts of burden. I took care to secure several, and put them in the cart.

When we had spent about an hour in getting forward, we found ourselves at the extremity of the wood, and a most singular phenomenon presented itself to our view; a small plain, or rather a grove of small bushes, to appearance almost covered with flakes of snow, lay extended before us. Little Francis was the first to call our attention to it, he being seated in the cart.

"Look, Father," cried he, "here is a place quite full of snow! Let me get down and make some snow-balls. Oh, how glad I am that we shall now have snow instead of the ugly rain which made us all so uncomfortable!"

I could not resist a hearty laugh. Though sure that what we saw could not, in the midst of such scorching heat, be snow, yet I was completely at a loss to explain the nature of what in colour and appearance bore so near a resemblance to it. Suddenly, however, a suspicion crossed my mind, and was soon confirmed by Fritz, who had darted forward on his onagra, and now returned with one hand filled with tufts of cotton, so that the whole surface of low bushes was in reality a plantation of that valuable article. The pods had burst from ripeness, and the winds had scattered around their flaky contents, so that the ground was strewed with them. They had gathered in tufts on the bushes, and the air was full of the gently-floating down.

The joy of this discovery was almost too great for utterance, and was shared by all but Francis, who was sorry to lose his pretty snow-balls. His mother, to soothe his regret, made the cotton into balls for him to play with, and promised him some new shirts. Then turning to me she poured out her kind heart in descriptions of all the comfortable things she should make for us, could I construct a spinning-wheel and then a loom for weaving.

We collected as much cotton as our bags would hold, and my wife filled her pockets with the seed to raise it in our garden at Tent House.

It was now time to proceed. We took a direction towards a point of land which skirted the wood of gourds, and, being high, commanded a view of the adjacent country. I conceived a wish to remove our establishment to the vicinity of the cotton plantation and the gourd wood, which furnished so many of the utensils for daily use throughout the family. I pleased myself in idea with the view of the different colonies of animals I had imagined, both winged and quadruped; and in this elevation of my fancy I even thought it might be practicable to erect a sort of farmhouse on the soil, which we might visit occasionally, and be welcomed by the agreeable sounds of the cackling of our feathered subjects, which would so forcibly remind us of the customs of our foresaken but ever-cherished country.

We accordingly soon reached the high ground, which I found in all respects favourable to my design. Behind, a thick forest gradually rose above us, which sheltered us from the north wind and insensibly declined towards the south, ending in a plain clothed luxuriantly with grass, shrubs, and plants, and watered by a refreshing rivulet, which was an incalculable advantage for our animals of every kind as well as for ourselves.

My plan for a building was approved by all, and we lost no time in pitching our tent and forming temporary accommodations for cooking our victuals. When we had refreshed ourselves with a meal, we each took up some useful occupation. My wife and the boys went to work with the cotton, which they thoroughly cleansed and cleared from bits of the pods or other foreign substance, and which was then put into the bags and served commodiously at night for bolsters and mattresses. I for my part resolved to look about in all directions, that I might completely understand what we should have to depend upon in this place in point of safety, salubrity, and general accommodation. I had also to find a tree that would suit for the proposed construction of a boat; and lastly, to meet if possible with a group of trees at such fit distances from each other as would assist me in my plan of erecting my farmhouse. I was fortunate enough in no long time to find in this last respect exactly what I wanted, and quite near to the spot we on many accounts had felt to be so enviable. But I was not equally successful as regards the boat, the trees in the vicinity being of too small a bulk to supply the depth necessary for keeping on the surface of the water. I returned to my companions, whom I found busily employed in preparing excellent beds of the cotton, upon which at an earlier hour than usual we all retired to rest.

## CHAPTER XVIII

The trees that I had chosen for the construction of my farm were all about one foot in diameter; their growth was tolerably regular, and they formed a rough parallelogram with the longest side to the sea, the length being twenty-four feet and the breadth sixteen. I cut little hollow places or mortises in the trunks, at the distance of ten feet, one above the other, to form two stories. The upper one I made a few inches shorter before than behind, that the roof might be in some degree shelving. I then inserted beams five inches in diameter respectively in the mortises, and thus formed the skeleton of my building. We next nailed some laths from tree to tree at equal distances from each other to form the roof, and I placed on them a covering composed of pieces of the bark of trees cut into the shape of tiles, and in a sloping position for the rain to run off in the wet season. As we had no great provision of iron nails, we used for the purpose the stronger pointed thorn of the acacia, which, we had discovered the day before. The tree, which bears an elegant flower, is known by the name of Acacia with three thorns, and it in reality exhibits, growing all together three strong sharp-pointed thorns, which might easily be used as weapons of defence. We cut down a quantity of them and laid them in the sun to dry, when they became as hard as iron, and were of essential service to our undertaking. We found great difficulty in peeling off a sufficient quantity of bark from trees to cover our roof. I began with cutting the bark entirely round at distances of about two feet all the length of the trunk. I next divided the intervals perpendicularly into two parts, which I separated from the tree by sliding a wedge under the corners to raise the bark by degrees. I next placed the pieces on the ground, with stones laid on them to prevent their curving, to dry in the sun. Lastly, I nailed them on the roof, where they overlapped each other like the slates or tiles on the roofs of the houses of our native land.

On this occasion we made another agreeable discovery. My wife took up the remaining chips of the bark for lighting a fire, supposing they would burn easily, and we were surprised by a delicious aromatic odour which perfumed the air. On examining the half-consumed substance, we found some of the pieces to contain turpentine and others gum-mastich, so that we might rely on a supply of these ingredients from the trees which had furnished the bark. It was less with a view to the gratifying our sense of smell, than with the hope of being able to secure a sort of pitch to complete our meditated boat, that we indulged our earnestness in the pursuit. The instinct of our goats, or the acuteness of their smell, discovered for us another acquisition of a no less pleasing quality. We observed with surprise that they ran from a considerable distance to throw themselves about on some particular chip of bark which lay on the ground, and which they began to chew and eat greedily. Jack seized a piece also, to find out, as he said, what could be the reason of so marked a preference as the goats had shown.

"Oh, it is indeed excellent," exclaimed he; "and I perceive that goats are animals of taste! Only try this little bit, brother Fritz, and tell us if it is not exactly like cinnamon?"

Fritz did as he was desired, and was of Jack's opinion. My wife and I then followed their example, and were convinced that it was cinnamon, though not so fine a sort as that from the isle of Ceylon.

This new commodity was certainly of no great importance to us, but we nevertheless regarded it with pleasure as an article that would serve to distinguish some day of particular rejoicing. Ernest and Francis asked to taste it also, and agreed with us that the occasional use of it would be agreeable. The tree from which we had taken our bark was old, and the cinnamon was no doubt the coarser flavoured on this account. I remember to have read that young trees produce this spice in much greater perfection.

During our next meal we amused ourselves with a retrospect of the different discoveries we had made that day. I had to relate what I knew on the subject of the nature of these new productions: the turpentine, the mastich, and the cinnamon.

When our meal and the lecture were both ended, we resumed with ardour our undertaking of the farm, which we continued without interruption for several days.

We formed the walls of our building with matted reeds, interwoven with pliant laths to the height of six feet. The remaining space to the roof was enclosed with only a simple grating, that the air and light might be admitted. A door was placed in the middle of the front. We next arranged the interior, with as much convenience as the shortness of the time and our reluctance to use all our timber would allow. We divided it half-way up by a partition wall, into two equal parts. The largest was intended for the sheep and goats, and the smallest for ourselves, when we should wish to pass a few days here. At the farther end of the stable we fixed a house for the fowls, and above it a sort of hay-loft for the forage. Before the door of the entrance we placed two benches, contrived as well as we could of laths and odd pieces of wood, that we might rest ourselves under the shade of the trees and enjoy the exquisite prospect which presented itself on all sides. Our own apartment was provided with a couple of the best bedsteads we could make of branches of trees, raised upon four legs two feet from the ground, and these were destined to receive our cotton mattresses. Our aim was to content ourselves for the present with these slight hints of a dwelling, and to consider hereafter what additions either of convenience or ornament could be made. All we were now anxious about was to provide a shelter for our animal colonists, which should encourage and fix them in the habit of assembling every evening in one place. For several days at first we took care to fill their troughs with their favourite food mixed with salt, and we agreed that we would return frequently to repeat this indirect mode of invitation for their society till they should be entirely fixed in their expectation of finding it.

I had imagined we could accomplish what we wished at the farm in three or four days. But we found that a whole week was necessary, and our victuals fell short before our work was done. We began to consider what remedy we could apply to so embarrassing a circumstance; I could not prevail upon myself to return to Falcon's Stream before I had completed my intentions at the farm, and the other objects of my journey. I had even come to the determination of erecting another building upon the site of Cape Disappointment. I therefore decided that on this trying occasion I would invest Fritz and Jack with the important mission. They were accordingly despatched to Falcon's Stream and to Tent House to fetch new supplies of cheese, ham, potatoes, dried fish, manioc bread for our subsistence, and also to distribute fresh food to the numerous animals we had left there. I directed one to mount the onagra, and the other the buffalo. My two knight-errants, proud of their embassy, set off with a brisk trot. At my desire they took with them the old ass to bring the load of provisions. Whether from the influence of climate or the example of his companion the onagra, our ass had lost much of his accustomed inactivity, which was the more important, as I intended to make a saddle for my wife to get on his back, and relieve herself occasionally from the fatigue of walking.

During the absence of our purveyors, I rambled with Ernest about the neighbouring soil, to make what new discoveries I could, and to procure if possible some coco-nuts or other addition to our store of provisions.

We followed the winding of a river we had remarked, and which conducted towards the centre of the wall of rocks. Our course was here interrupted by an extensive marsh which bordered a small lake, the aspect of which was enchantingly picturesque. I perceived with joyful surprise that the whole surface of this swampy soil was covered with a kind of wild rice, ripe on the stalk, and which attracted the voracity of large flocks of birds. As we approached, a loud rustling was heard, and we distinguished on the wing bustards and great numbers of smaller birds, with the names of which we were unacquainted. We succeeded in bringing down five or six of them, and I was pleased to remark in Ernest a justness of aim that promised well for the future. The habits of his mind discovered themselves on this as on many previous occasions. He betrayed no ardour, he did everything with a deliberation that almost seemed to imply sluggishness; yet the coolness and constancy he applied to every attempt he had to engage in, so effectually assisted his judgement, that he was sure to arrive at a more perfect execution than the other boys. He had practised but little in the study of how to fire a gun to best advantage; but Ernest was a silent enquirer and observer, and accordingly his first essays were generally crowned with success. In this affair, however, of the birds, his skill would have proved fruitless, if Jack's young jackal, which had followed us in our walk, had not plunged courageously into the swamp and brought out the birds as they fell.

At a small distance was also the monkey, who had taken his post on Ponto's back. Presently we saw him jump off and smell earnestly along the ground among some thick-growing plants, then pluck off something with his two paws and eat of it voraciously. We ran to the spot to see what it could be, when, to the infinite relief of our parched palates, we found he had discovered there the largest and finest kind of strawberry, which is called in Europe the Chili or Pine strawberry.

On this occasion the proud creature, man, generously condescended to be the imitator of a monkey. We threw ourselves upon the ground, as near to the monkey as we could creep, and devoured as fast as we could swallow, till we felt sufficiently refreshed. Many of these strawberries were of an enormous size and Ernest with his usual coolness, and I must needs confess there was no want of his constancy either, devoured an immense quantity. He, however, recollected his absent friends, and filled a small gourd shell we had brought with us with the finest fruit, and then covered them with leaves and tied them down with a tendril from a neighbouring plant, that he might present them in perfection to his mother. I, on my part, gathered a specimen of the rice to offer, that she might inform us if it was fit for culinary purposes.

After pursuing our way a little farther along the marsh, we reached the lake, which we had descried with so much pleasure from a distance, and whose banks being overgrown with thick underwood, were necessarily concealed from the momentary view we had leisure to take of surrounding objects, particularly as the lake was situated in a deep and abrupt valley. No traveller who is not a native of Switzerland can conceive the emotion which trembled at my heart as I contemplated this limpid, azure, undulating body of water, the faithful miniature of so many grand originals, which I had probably lost sight of for ever! My eyes swam with tears! "How glad I am to see a lake! I could almost think myself in Switzerland, Father!" said Ernest.

Alas, a single glance upon the surrounding pictures, the different characters of the trees, the vast ocean in the distance, destroyed the momentary illusion, and brought back our ideas to the painful reality that we were strangers in a desert island!

Another sort of object now presented itself to confirm the certainty that we were no longer inhabitants of Europe. It was the appearance of a quantity of swans which glided over the surface of the lake; but their colour, instead of white, like those of our country, was a jetty black; and their plumage had so high a gloss as to produce, reflected in the water, the most astonishing effect. The six large feathers of the wing of this bird are white, exhibiting a singular contrast to the rest of the body. In other respects these creatures were remarkably like those of Europe. We remained a long time in silent admiration of the scene. Some of the swans pursued their course magnificently on the bosom of the blue water;

others stopped and seemed to hold deliberations with their companions, or to admire themselves or caress each other; many young ones followed in the train of the parent bird, who frequently turned half-round in execution of her watchful and matronly office. This was a spectacle which I could not allow to be interrupted by bloodshed, though Ernest would have been ready to fire upon the swans if I had not absolutely forbidden the attempt; at the same time I consoled him with the promise that we would endeavour to obtain a pair of the interesting creatures for our establishment at Falcon's Stream.

Ponto just at this moment dragged out of the water a bird he had seized. We ran to examine it, and our surprise was extreme on remarking the singularity of its appearance. It was somewhat in shape like an otter, and, like the tribe of water-birds, web-footed. Its tail was long and erect, and covered with a soft kind of hair; the head was very small, and the ears and eyes were almost invisible. To these more ordinary characters was added a long flat bill, like that of a duck, which protruded from its snout, and produced so ludicrous an effect that we could not resist a hearty laugh. All the science of the learned Ernest, joined with my own, was insufficient to ascertain the name and nature of this animal. We had no resource but to remain ignorant; in the meantime we christened it by the name of Beast with a bill, and decided that it should be carefully stuffed and preserved.

We now began to look for the shortest path for rejoining our companions at the farm, which we reached at the same time with Fritz and Jack, who had well performed the object of their journey, and were received by all with satisfaction. We produced our offering of strawberries and our specimen of rice, which were welcomed with shouts of pleasure and surprise.

The beast with a bill was next examined with eager curiosity, and then laid aside for the plan I had formed. My wife proceeded to pluck and salt the birds we had killed, reserving one fresh for our supper, which we partook of together upon the benches before the door of our new habitation. We filled the stable with forage, laid a large provision of grain for the fowls within their house, and began arrangements for our departure.

The following day we took a silent leave of our animals and directed our course towards Cape Disappointment. On entering Monkey Wood, innumerable animals of the species from which it derives its name began to scamper away, grinding their teeth in sign of anger at our approach. We pursued our way, and arrived shortly after at the eminence we were in pursuit of in the vicinity of Cape Disappointment. We ascended it, and found it in every respect adapted to our wishes. From this eminence we had a view over the country which surrounded Falcon's Stream in one direction, and in others of a richly diversified extent of landscape comprehending sea, land, and rocks. When we had paused for a short time upon the exhaustless beauties of the scene, we agreed with one voice that it should be on this spot we would build our second cottage. A spring of the clearest water issued from the soil near the summit, and flowed over its sloping side, forming in its rapid course agreeable cascades. I presented my children with an appropriate word: "Let us build here," exclaimed I, "and call the spot Arcadia!" to which my wife and all agreed.

We lost no time in again setting to work upon this additional arduous undertaking. Our experience at the farm enabled us to proceed in it with rapidity, and our success was in every respect more complete. The building contained a dining-room, two bed-chambers, two stables, and a store-room for preserving all kinds of provisions for man and beast. We formed the roof square, with four sloping sides, and the whole had really the appearance of an European cottage, and was finished in the short space of six days.

## CHAPTER XIX

Our Arcadia being entirely completed, what remained to be done was to fix on a tree fit for my project of a boat. After much search, I at length found one in most respects suitable to my views.

It was, however, no very encouraging prospect I had before me, being nothing less than the stripping off a piece of the bark that should be eighteen feet in length and five in diameter. I now found my rope ladder of signal service. We fastened it by one end to the nearest branches, and it enabled us to work with the saw, as might be necessary, at any height from the ground. Accordingly we cut quite round the trunk in two places, and then took a perpendicular slip from the whole length between the circles. By this means we could introduce the proper utensils for raising the rest by degrees till it was entirely separated. We toiled with increasing anxiety, at every moment dreading that we should not be able to preserve it from breaking or being injured by our tools. When we had loosened about half, we supported it by means of cords and pulleys, and when all was at length detached we let it down gently, and with joy beheld it lying safe on the grass. Our business was next to mould it to our purpose while the substance continued moist and flexible.

The boys observed that we had now nothing more to do than to nail a plank at each end, and our boat would be as complete as those used by the savages. But, for my own part, I could not be contented with a mere roll of bark for a boat, and when I reminded them of the paltry figure it would make following the pinnace, I heard not another word about the further pains and trouble, and they asked eagerly for my instructions. I made them assist me to saw the bark in the middle, the length of several feet from the ends. These two parts I folded over till they ended in a point, naturally raised. I kept them in this form by the help of the strong fish-glue, and pieces of wood nailed fast over the whole. This operation tended to widen the boat in the middle, and thus render it of too flat a form. This we counteracted by straining a cord all round, which again reduced it to the due proportion, and in this state we put it to the sun to harden and fix. Many things were still wanting to the completion of my undertaking, but I had not with me proper utensils. I therefore, despatched the boys to Tent House to fetch the sledge, and convey the boat there for our better convenience in finishing.

Before our departure for Tent House we collected several new plants for the kitchen-garden. We also made another trip to the narrow strait at the end of the wall of rocks, resolved, as I before mentioned, to plant there a sort of fortification of trees, which should produce the double effect of discouraging the invasion of savages and of allowing us to keep our pigs on the other side, and thus secure our different plantations from the chance of injury. We accomplished this to our entire satisfaction, and in addition we placed a slight drawbridge across the river beyond the narrow pass, which we could let down or take up at pleasure on our side. We now hastened our return to Arcadia, and after a night's repose we loaded the sledge with the boat and other things, and returned to Tent House.

As soon as possible we resumed the completion of the boat. In two days she had received the addition of a keel, a lining of wood, a small flat floor, benches, a small mast and triangular sail, a rudder, and a thick coat of pitch on the outside, so that the first time we saw her in the water we were all delighted at the charming appearance she made.

Our cow in the meantime had brought forth a bull calf. I pierced its nostril, as I had so successfully practised with the buffalo, and the animal gave promise of future docility and strength.

We had still two months in prospect before the rainy season, and we employed them in completing our abode in the grotto. We made the internal divisions of planks, and that which separated us from the stables of stone, to protect us from the offensive smell of the animals. Our task was difficult, but from habit it became easier every day. We took care to collect or manufacture a sufficient quantity of all sorts of materials, such as beams and planks, reeds and twigs for matting, pieces of gypsum for plaster,

&c. At length the time of the rainy season was near at hand, and this time we thought of it with pleasure, as the period that would put us in possession of the enjoyments we had procured by such unremitting industry and fatigue. We had an inexpressible longing to find ourselves domiciled and at leisure.

We plastered over the walls of the principal apartments on each side with the greatest care, finishing them by pressure with a flat smooth board. This portion of our work amused us all so much, that we began to think we might venture a step further in the question of European luxury, and we agreed that we would attempt to make some carpets with the hair of our goats. To this purpose we smoothed the ground in the rooms we intended to furnish in this manner. We then spread it with some sail-cloth, which my wife had joined in breadths, and fitted exactly. We next strewed the goats' hair, mixed with wool obtained from the sheep over the whole. On this surface we threw some hot water, in which a strong cement had been dissolved. The whole was then rolled up, and was beaten for a considerable time with hard sticks. The sail-cloth was now unrolled, and the inside again sprinkled, rolled, and beaten as before. This process was continued till the substance had become a sort of felt which could be separated from the sail-cloth. We put it in the sun to harden, and found we had produced a very tolerable substitute for a European carpet. We completed two of them, one for our parlour an the other for our drawing-room, as we jocosely named them, both of which were completely fit for our reception by the time the rains had set in.

All we had suffered during the preceding rainy

season doubled the value of the comforts and conveniences with which we were now surrounded. We were never tired of admiring our warm and well-arranged appartments, lighted with windows, and well secured with doors from wind and rain, and our granary filled with more than a sufficient winter supply of food for ourselves and for our cattle. In the morning our first care was to feed the cattle and give them drink. After this we assembled in the parlour, where prayers were read and breakfast immediately served. We then adjourned to the common room, where all sorts of industry went forward, and which contained the spinning-wheel and loom I had, though with indifferent success, constructed to gratify my wife. Here all united in the business of producing different kinds of things, which she afterwards made into apparel. I had also contrived to construct a turning-machine, having used for the purpose one of the small cannon wheels, with the help of which the boys and I managed to produce some neat utensils for general use. After dinner our work was resumed till night, when we lighted candles, which, as they cost no more than our own trouble in collecting and manufacturing the materials, we did not refuse ourselves the pleasure of using many at a time. We had formed a convenient portion of our dwelling into a small chapel, in which we left the crystals as produced by nature, and they exhibited a wonderful assemblage of colonnades, porticoes, altars, which, when the place was lighted to supply the want of a window, presented a truly enchanting spectacle. Divine service was performed in it regularly every Sunday. I had raised a sort of pulpit, from which I pronounced such discourses as I had framed for the instruction of my affectionate group of auditors.

Jack and Francis had a natural inclination for music. I did the most I could in making a flageolet apiece for them of two reeds, on which they so frequently practised as to attain a tolerable proficiency. They accompanied their mother, who had a sweet-toned voice, the volume of which was doubled by the echoes of the grottos, and they produced together a very pleasing little concert.

Thus, as will be perceived, we had made the first steps towards a condition of civilization. Separated from society, condemned perhaps to pass the remainder of life in this desert island, we yet possessed the means of happiness. We had abundance of all the necessaries, and many of the comforts desired by human beings. We had fixed habits of activity and industry; we were in ourselves contented; our bodily health and strength increased from day to day; the sentiment of tender attachment was perfect in every heart; and we every day acquired some new and still improving channel for the exertion of our physical and moral faculties.

Nearly two years had elapsed without our perceiving the smallest trace of civilized or savage man, without the appearance of a single vessel or canoe upon the vast sea by which we are surrounded. Ought we then to indulge a hope that we shall once again behold the face of a fellow-creature? We encourage serenity and thankfulness in each other, and wait with resignation the event!

## POSTSCRIPT BY THE EDITOR

I have presented the public, and in particular the sons of families, with the part I had in my possession of the journal of the Swiss pastor, who, with his family, were shipwrecked on a desert island. It cannot escape the observation of the parents who will read the work, that it exhibits a lively picture of the happiness which does not fail to result from the practice of moral virtues. Thus, in a situation that seemed calculated to produce despair, we see piety, affection, industry, and a generous concern for fellow-sufferers, capable of forming the basis of an unexpected state of serenity and happiness. We also see the advantage of including in the education of boys such a knowledge of the natural productions of the earth, of the various combinations by which they may be rendered serviceable, and of the use of tools, of every kind, as may qualify them to assist others or preserve themselves under every possible occurrence of adversity or danger. It now remains for me to inform the reader by what means the journal of the Swiss pastor came into my possession.

Three or four years subsequent to the occurrence

of the shipwreck of the pastor and his family, an English transport was driven by the violence of a tempest upon the same shore. The name of the vessel was the Adventurer commanded by Captain Johnson. It was on a voyage from New Zealand to the eastern coast of North America, by Otheite, in the South Seas, to fetch a cargo of skins and furs for China, and to proceed from Canton to England. A violent tempest of several days' duration drove it from its track. The vessel beat about in unknown seas for many days, and was now so injured by the weather that the best hope of the captain and his company was to get into some port where they might refit. They at length discovered a rocky coast, and as the wind had somewhat abated they made with all speed for the shore. When within a short distance they cast their anchor, and put out a boat containing some of the officers to examine the coast and find a place for landing. They rowed backward and forward for some time without success, on account of the rocky nature of the coast. At length they turned a promontory, and perceived a bay whose calm water seemed to invite their approach. This was the Safety Bay of the wrecked islanders. The boat put on shore, and the officers with astonishment beheld the traces of the abode of man. A handsome well-conditioned pinnace and a small boat were there at anchor. Near the strand, under a rock, was a tent, and farther on in the rock a house-door and windows announced European comforts and workmanship. The officers advanced towards the spot, and were met half-way by a man of middle age, dressed like a European and armed with a gun. The stranger accosted them with friendly tones and gestures. He spoke first German, and then some words in English. Lieutenant Bell, one of the English officers, who spoke the German language, answered. A mutual confidence immediately ensued. We need not add that the stranger was the father of the family whose adventures are narrated in the previous pages. His wife and children happened at the moment to be at Falcon's Stream. He had discovered the English ship in the morning with his glass, and, unwilling to alarm his family, had come, perceiving she bore that way, alone to the coast.

After an interchange of cordial greetings, and a hospitable reception of the officers at the grotto, the Swiss pastor put his journal into the hands of Lieutenant Bell, to be conveyed to Captain Johnson, that he also might become acquainted with the story of the solitary islanders. After an hour's conversation the newly-made friends separated, in the pleasing expectation of meeting again on the following day. But Heaven had otherwise ordained.

During the night the tempest revived with new terrors. The Adventurer dragged her anchor, and was obliged to steer for safety to the bosom of the ocean. As there was no favourable change of weather for several days, the vessel was driven so far from the coast of Safety Bay as to leave no possibility of returning, and Captain Johnson was compelled to renounce the gratification of seeing this most interesting family, or of proposing to convey them all to Europe.

Captain Johnson brought the journal of the Swiss pastor to England, from whence it was transmitted to a friend in Switzerland, who had deemed its contents an instructive lesson to the world. There was found attached to the journal a rough sketch of the features of the island which Lieutenant Bell thinks the Swiss pastor informed him was executed by his son Fritz. Unfortunately, it went astray, so that it cannot be presented to the young readers of this journal.

At a later time, the Pastor and his family were again heard of. Their island became a regular place of call for trading ships; and as prosperity increased, the Pastor was able to let his studious son Ernest proceed to Europe to pursue a course of professional study at one of the universities, where he attained to high distinction. The other sons married and remained with their parents as prosperous planters on their loved island home, to which Ernest also ultimately returned, bringing with him as wife, his cousin Henrietta.

A word should be said about the title by which this entrancing record is generally known. Those who were responsible for publishing it, and giving the story to the world, could not but be struck by the many points of similarity between the adventures of the Swiss Pastor's family and those of the famous Robinson Crusoe. They therefore named the book The Swiss Family Robinson Crusoe, which in course of time became contracted to the title by which the book is now known, The Swiss Family Robinson.